Forces and motion

Advanced Physics Project for Independent Learning

Student's Guide

KU-372-012

ohn Murray
n association with
nner London Education Authority

How to use this student's guide

This is a programme for independent learning. It is not a textbook: it is a guide to using texts, experiments and other resources to help you to learn about forces, motion and energy.

There are sections of text in this guide which are to be read as in any other book, but much of the guide is concerned with helping you through activities designed to produce effective learning when you work independently. For a fuller explanation of the way APPIL is written you should read the Student's Handbook. What follows is a brief summary.

Objectives

What is to be learnt is stated at the beginning of each chapter — a general statement of what you will be doing, and more detailed objectives to be achieved. The *objectives* are particularly important, because they tell you what you should be able to do when you have finished working through the chapter, and so give you extra help in organising your learning. You will probably wish to refer to them when you have finished each chapter.

Experiments

These are a very important part of the course. The experiments in each chapter are listed at the beginning of the chapter, with an indication of the approximate *laboratory time* required for setting up the apparatus and taking readings. Each experiment is referred to in the text at the most appropriate time. You should aim to organise your work so that it can be done at that time. Full details of experiments are given at the end of the unit. Record your results, graphically or in some other way, and your conclusions. There is no value in copying out the instructions given, but notes on special procedures, and any details which might be useful for revision, should be made.

Questions

Self-assessment questions

These test your understanding of the work you have done, and will help you to check your progress. They are not intended to be difficult: you should be able to answer most of them quite easily.

The answers to self-assessment questions are given at the end of the book, but if you look at the answer before you have tried the question you will not be involved in the learning process and your learning may suffer.

Development questions

These are included to involve you in a proof or idea which is being developed in the text.

Answers to these questions are in the text or, for questions marked with an asterisk, at the end of the book. Involving yourself in the development helps you to learn: just looking at the answer is not so effective.

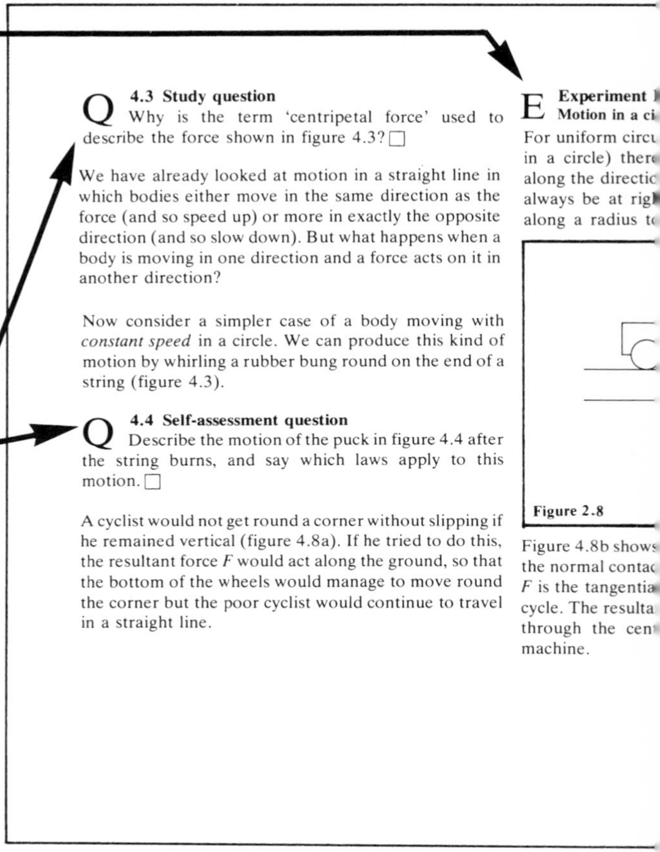

Q 4.3 Study question
Why is the term 'centripetal force' used to describe the force shown in figure 4.3? □

We have already looked at motion in a straight line in which bodies either move in the same direction as the force (and so speed up) or more in exactly the opposite direction (and so slow down). But what happens when a body is moving in one direction and a force acts on it in another direction?

Now consider a simpler case of a body moving with *constant speed* in a circle. We can produce this kind of motion by whirling a rubber bung round on the end of a string (figure 4.3).

Q 4.4 Self-assessment question
Describe the motion of the puck in figure 4.4 after the string burns, and say which laws apply to this motion. □

A cyclist would not get round a corner without slipping if he remained vertical (figure 4.8a). If he tried to do this, the resultant force *F* would act along the ground, so that the bottom of the wheels would manage to move round the corner but the poor cyclist would continue to travel in a straight line.

E Experiment **Motion in a ci**
For uniform circu in a circle) there along the directic always be at rig along a radius to

Figure 2.8

Figure 4.8b shows the normal contac *F* is the tangentia cycle. The resulta through the cen machine.

Study questions

For these you will need to use resources apart from this guide: for example, textbooks or experimental results. General references are given to basic books at the start of each chapter. You are not expected to consult all the references given, but you should always use more than one when possible. An example of the use of book references is given in chapter 1.

constant speed
ent acceleration
cceleration must
on and directed

es a corner. *R* is
n the cycle, and
e ground on the
a force *P* acting
e rider and the

This type of question usually requires longer answers
than the others. These answers, in many cases, form a
basis for your notes for the final examination and are
therefore very important. Full answers are not usually
given in this guide, though hints and partial answers are
sometimes given (these questions are marked with an
asterisk). Your answers to study questions should be
handed in regularly for marking.

Extensions

Extensions are provided for several reasons.
(a) To provide additional material of general interest,
e.g. applications.
(b) To provide more detailed treatment of some topics.
(c) To provide additional topics, or extensions of core
material, to cover the requirements of a particular
examination board. In this case, the section is marked
SYLLABUS EXTENSION and will be essential study
for some students, although others may find it of value.
You should consult your teacher if you are not certain
whether a particular syllabus extension is appropriate
for you.

Use of resources

Audio-visual aids. Several 8 mm film loops are listed in
this guide. These are included to supplement your
experimental observations. Notes and questions
accompany the film loops.
Computer programs. A computer program is recommended for use in the revision appendix. You should ask
your teacher if this is available.
Background reading. This refers to books which are
useful for a more detailed study of certain topics. They
are also often interesting to read in their own right, and
sometimes put the physics of the syllabus in its
historical, social and technological context.

Questions on objectives

These are groups of questions which come at the end of
each chapter, and are related to the objectives at the
beginning of each chapter. Answering these will help
you to tell whether you have achieved the objectives.

End-of-unit test

This is to enable your teacher to check the value of the
course to you. You will be asked to do this test when
you have completed the unit, and will be given details at
the appropriate time.

Organising your time

In this programme of work there is a variety of
activities. Some of them, like experiments, need a
laboratory, and you will also need to use the library.
You must, therefore, organise your time so that you can
make the best use of the resources available.

When you start a chapter, look through it and see what
activities are included, then allocate each activity a time
on your work schedule. Make sure, for example, that
you do the experiments when you are timetabled in a
laboratory. Follow the sequence in this guide if you can,
but this may not always be possible.

In the introduction, and at the beginning of each
chapter, you will find the recommended time for
completion of the work in each chapter. These times are
given in units of one week. This assumes that you spend
a minimum of 10 hours each week on physics, divided
between class time, private study and home study. It is
important to try to complete the unit in the stated time.
The *progress monitor* will help you plan your time.

Introduction to the unit

In this unit you will examine how forces applied to a body can affect its motion.

As this unit is one of the recommended starting points for the course, there is a preliminary section, 'Starting block', which reviews some of your earlier physics studies which are relevant to this unit, and includes a preliminary test and advice on how to fill any gaps in your knowledge.

Chapter 1 is mainly a revision chapter. It will remind you of the basic ideas about types of force and the methods used to measure force and motion.

Chapter 2 introduces Newton's laws of motion and methods of investigating these laws experimentally.

Chapter 3 is a study of the momentum and energy changes which occur when bodies interact with each other. The results of this study will be applied to the principles of powered flight, and of safety design in cars.

Chapter 4 considers the forces acting on bodies travelling in circular paths and discusses relevant applications, from spin driers to orbiting satellites.

Chapter 5 discusses how forces can change the rotational motion of a body. You will consider how these rotational changes depend on where the forces are acting and on the mass, shape and size of the body.

Recommended study times

You should spend between 6 and 7 weeks on this unit, divided roughly as follows.

Chapter 1   1 week
Chapter 2   1 week
Chapter 3   2 weeks
Chapter 4 $1\frac{1}{2}$ weeks
Chapter 5 $1\frac{1}{2}$ weeks

In independent learning, students progress through the text at different rates and if you have remembered your earlier studies in mechanics, you will find that you can progress quickly through Chapters 1 and 2, and the first part of Chapter 3.

Contents

Starting block

It is assumed in this unit that you have studied physics before, so the unit will build on and extend your present knowledge. Since you may have forgotten some of the things you learnt, or there may be a few things you are not sure about, this section is designed to help you to revise, re-learn or learn what you need to know to make the best use of this unit.

Start by reading the pre-requisite objectives: these are the things you need to be able to do before you begin work on the main part of the unit.

Then work through the preliminary test, which consists of questions based on the pre-requisite objectives. Work quickly through all parts of the test without reference to books or to any other person. The aim of the test is to enable you to check up on what you know now, so that you can find and fill up any gaps in your own knowledge.

Mark your own test when you have finished, following the marking instructions. Then read the directions for using your test result, and do any follow-up work that is recommended for you.

When you have done this, you will be able to start chapter one with the confidence of knowing that you are ready to tackle new work.

Pre-requisite objectives

Before starting this unit you should be able to:

1 Identify, for a given situation,
(a) the nature and cause of each of the forces acting,
(b) the direction and place of action of each force.

2 Define the moment of a force and state the law of moments for parallel forces.

3 Use the following scientific terms correctly:
resultant, component, resolve, scalar, vector.

4 Distinguish between vector and scalar quantities.

5. Determine the resolved part of a vector quantity in any given direction.

6 Use the parallelogram and triangle of vectors to solve problems involving vector quantities, including relative velocity.

7 Use the following scientific terms correctly, and state their SI units:
speed, velocity, distance, displacement, acceleration.

8 Explain the difference between average speed (or velocity) and instantaneous speed (or velocity).

9 Solve problems on linear motion and projectile motion, using:
(a) displacement-time and velocity-time graphs,
(b) equations of linear motion.

10 Define the following physical quantities and state the SI units in which they are measured:
kinetic energy, potential energy, work, power, efficiency.

11 State, in your own words, the law of conservation of energy.

12 Identify, in a given situation,
(a) the sources of energy,
(b) the energy transformations taking place.

13 Solve problems based on objectives 10, 11 and 12.

Preliminary test

There are three types of question in this test, coded as follows:

MC Multiple choice. Select the single best answer.
MR Multiple response. Select all the correct answers.
NUM Numerical answer. Work out the answer and write it down, including the unit where appropriate.

Part A Forces

Questions 1–4 *MR*

Figures P1 to P4 show situations in which external forces act on a body. Which of the forces (A–F) below are acting on the bodies specified in questions 1–4?

A Weight (gravitational force).
B Friction between solids.
C Resistance forces in liquids.
D Air resistance.
E Upthrust (due to displacement of a gas or liquid).
F Reaction force exerted by the ground or other support.

1 The runner in figure P1.

2 The gymnast in figure P2.

3 The astronaut in figure P3.

4 The yacht in figure P4.

Figure P1

Figure P3

Figure P2

Figure P4

5 *MR* For which of the following actions is a resultant force required?
A Slowing down a moving body.
B Changing the direction in which a body is moving.
C Maintaining the constant velocity of a body moving across a rough horizontal surface.

6 *MR* Which of the following make use of friction?
A The clutch plate of a car.
B Walking.
C Slowing down a lunar module in space.

7 *MC* Which one of the systems (A–D) in figure P5 forms a couple?

8 *NUM* A uniform half-metre rule is freely pivoted at the 20 centimetre mark. It balances horizontally when a force of 0.2 newton pulls down at the 5 centimetre mark. Calculate the pull of the earth on the rule (the weight of the rule).

Part B Vectors

9 *MR* Which of the following are vector quantities?
A Weight.
B Mass.
C Velocity.
D Speed.

10 *MC* Figure P6 shows five different arrangements (A–E) of two forces acting on a body P. Which arrangement produces the largest resultant force?

11 *MC* Figure P7 shows five different arrangements (A–E) of three forces acting on a body P. If P remains at rest, which arrangement correctly represents the forces acting on it?

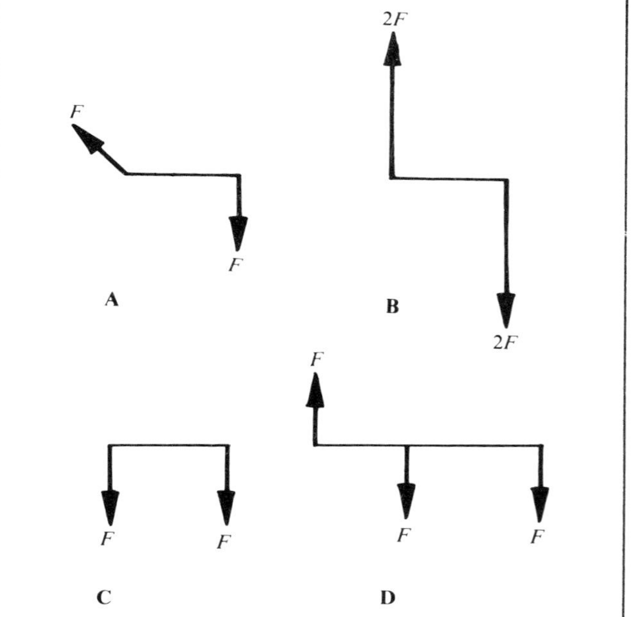

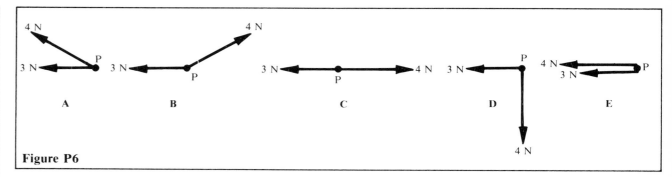

Figure P6

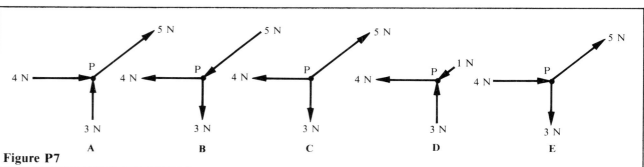

Figure P7

Figure P5

12 *NUM* A square ABCD has forces of 50 newtons and 80 newtons acting at A towards B and D respectively. Determine, by scale drawing or otherwise, the magnitude of the resultant force.

Questions 13 and 14 *NUM*
A nail projects horizontally from a vertical wall. A cord attached to its head is pulled downwards at an angle of 30° to the wall with a force of 6.0 newtons.

13 Find, by scale drawing or otherwise, the vertical downward force exerted by the cord on the nail.

14 Find, by scale drawing or otherwise, the force exerted by the cord tending to pull the nail out of the wall.

Questions 15 and 16 *NUM*
A body of mass 100 grams is held at rest on a smooth plane, inclined at 30° to the horizontal, by a force applied horizontally.

15 Draw a diagram showing the forces acting on the body and, using the triangle of forces rule or otherwise, find the magnitude of the applied force (take the pull of the earth on 100 grams to be 1.0 newton).

16 What is the magnitude and direction of the least force necessary to keep the body at rest on the plane?

17 *NUM* An aircraft has a velocity of 198 kilometres per hour at right angles to a strong wind. The velocity of the aircraft is 202 kilometres per hour relative to the earth. What is the velocity of the wind relative to the earth?

Part C Kinematics

18 *MR* The graph in figure P8 shows how the speed of a cyclist changes with time as he travels in a straight line. Which of the following statements is/are FALSE?

A The cyclist accelerates during the first 6.0 seconds.
B The cyclist travels at uniform speed during the second 6.0 seconds.
C The cyclist slows down after 12 seconds.
D The cyclist travels further while slowing down than while accelerating.
E The cyclist travels further while accelerating than while at uniform speed.

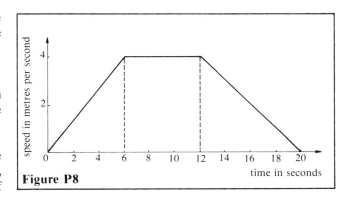

Figure P8

19 *MR* The graph in figure P9 represents the motion of a car travelling *in a straight line* towards and away from a stationary observer. Which of the following statements is/are true?

A The car reverses for a time of 9.0 seconds.
B The car is at rest for a time of 2.0 seconds.
C The distance of the car from the observer after 2.0 seconds is 15 metres.
D The total distance the car travels is 25 metres.
E The maximum speed of the car is greater than 10 metres per second.

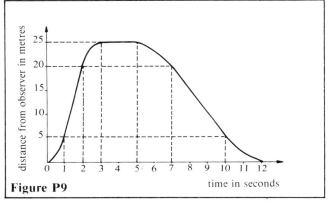

Figure P9

Questions 20 and 21 *NUM*
A body moving in a straight line with constant velocity for 4.0 seconds covers a distance of 80 metres, and then slows down uniformly, coming to rest after a further period of 2.0 seconds.

20 Find the initial velocity of the body (by drawing a velocity-time graph or otherwise).

21 Find the distance the body travelled in 6.0 seconds (by drawing a velocity-time graph or otherwise).

22 *NUM* A car is accelerated uniformly from rest at 2.0 metres per second squared. Calculate the distance travelled in the first 5.0 seconds of its motion.

Questions 23–25 *NUM*

A ball is thrown vertically upwards with a velocity of 20 metres per second (take *g* as 10 metres per second squared).

23 What is the acceleration of the ball?

24 How high does the ball rise?

25 How long does it take the ball to return to the thrower, from the time it left his hand?

Questions 26–28 *MC*

The two balls X and Y in figure P10 are both initially 5 metres above the ground. At the same moment that Y is dropped, X is shot off the ledge horizontally with an initial velocity of 6.0 metres per second. (Take *g* as 10 metres per second squared)

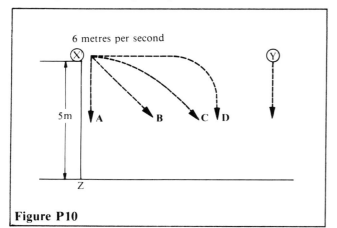

Figure P10

26 Which of the dotted lines (A–D) in figure P10 best shows the path of X as it travels from its starting position?

27 Which of the following statements is true?
A Y reaches the ground first.
B X reaches the ground first.
C X and Y reach the ground at the same time.

28 How far from the base of the ledge, Z, does ball X hit the ground?
A Less than 1 metre.
B 1 metre.
C 3 metres.
D 5 metres.
E 6 metres.

Part D Work, energy and power

29 *MR* Which of the following must be known in order to calculate the work done by a force?
A The magnitude of the force.
B The moment of a force about a point.
C The distance moved by the force along its line of action.
D The resolved components of the force in the horizontal and vertical directions.

30 *MC* An engine exerts a force of 5000 newtons, moving its point of application 5 metres in the direction of the force. The work done by the engine is
A   250 joules.
B   1000 joules.
C   4995 joules.
D   5005 joules.
E   25 000 joules.

31 *MC* A boy whose weight is 600 newtons runs up a flight of stairs 10 metres high in a time of 12 seconds. The average power used to climb the stairs is

A   72 watts.
B   500 watts.
C   720 watts.
D 5000 watts.
E 7200 watts.

32 *MR* A spacecraft returning to earth is 20 000 kilometres above the surface of the earth and is being attracted by the earth. If no engines are being fired on the spacecraft, it will be gaining

A potential energy.
B kinetic energy.
C speed.

33 *MC* An object is dropped vertically from rest and takes 1.0 second to reach the ground. Taking the potential energy of the object at ground level to be zero, then 0.5 second before hitting the ground the object will have

A equal potential and kinetic energies.
B more kinetic than potential energy.
C more potential than kinetic energy.
D half its original potential energy.

34 *MC* A sprinter of mass 50 kilograms runs at a speed of 8 metres per second. What is his kinetic energy?

A   400 joules.
B   500 joules.
C 1600 joules.
D 3200 joules.
E 4000 joules.

35 *NUM* What is the increase in potential energy of a climber of mass 75 kilograms after he has climbed from sea level to the summit of Snowdon at 1000 metres? (Take g as 10 metres per second squared, i.e. 10 newtons per kilogram.)

36 *NUM* A car is generating 7.5 kilowatts to travel along a horizontal road at a uniform speed of 15 metres per second. What is the frictional force it is overcoming?

Marking

Compare your answers with those given below, and give yourself one mark for each fully correct answer. To be fully correct, only the one right answer should be given for multiple choice questions, all the right answers and no wrong ones for multiple response questions, and the unit as well as the number for numerical questions. Add up your marks for each part of the test separately.

Answers

Part A *8 marks*

1 A, B, D, E, F (If your only mistake was to leave out E, count your answer as correct. The upthrust of the air is very small.)
2 A, B, E, F
3 A (the astronaut is in free fall)
4 A, C, D, E
5 A, B, C
6 A, B
7 B
8 0.6 newton

Part B *9 marks*

 9 A, C
10 E
11 C
12 94 newtons
13 5.2 newtons
14 3.0 newtons
15 Figure P11 shows the forces acting on the body.
    Applied force = 1.0×tan 30° newton
                  = 0.58 newton
16 The least force necessary to keep the body at rest is 0.50 newton, up the plane (figure P12).
17 40 kilometres per hour

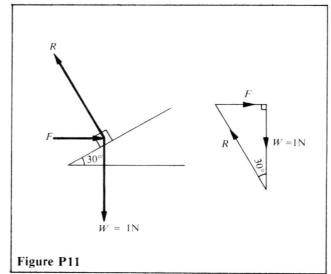

Figure P11

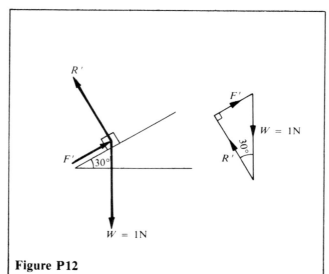

Figure P12

Part C *11 marks*

18 E
19 B, E
20 20 metres per second
21 100 metres
22 25 metres
23 −10 metres per second squared
24 20 metres
25 4.0 seconds
26 C
27 C
28 E

Part D *8 marks*

29 A, C
30 E
31 B
32 B, C
33 C (since the object is accelerating from rest, in half of the time it will cover less than half of the distance)
34 C
35 7.5×10^5 joules or 0.75 megajoules
36 500 newtons

Using the test results

The pre-requisite objectives were tested as follows.

Objectives 1 and 2	Part A
Objectives 3, 4, 5, and 6	Part B
Objectives 7, 8, and 9	Part C
Objectives 10, 11, 12, and 13	Part D

Your marks in the preliminary test indicate whether you need to do some follow-up work before starting chapter 1. The flowchart will direct you along your own personal route through any necessary revision sections.

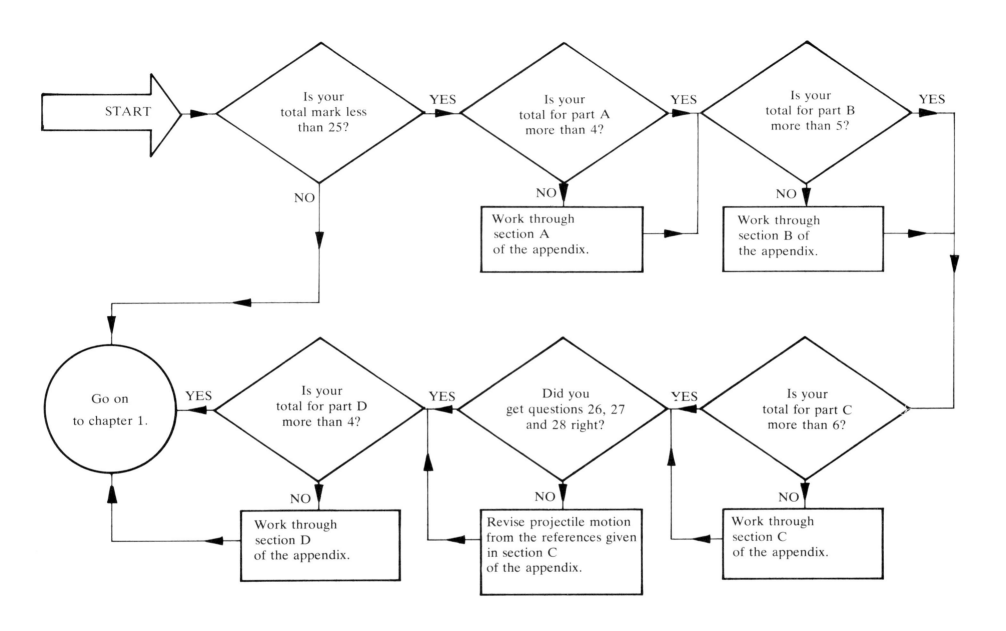

START

Is your total mark less than 25?

YES — Is your total for part A more than 4?

YES — Is your total for part B more than 5?

YES

NO

Work through section A of the appendix.

NO

Work through section B of the appendix.

Go on to chapter 1.

YES — Is your total for part D more than 4?

YES — Did you get questions 26, 27 and 28 right?

YES — Is your total for part C more than 6?

NO

Work through section D of the appendix.

NO

Revise projectile motion from the references given in section C of the appendix.

NO

Work through section C of the appendix.

Chapter

Aim

This chapter will enable you to review your knowledge of different types of force, to study briefly how forces can be measured, and to learn some simple methods for analysing the motion of bodies.

Measuring forces and analysing motion

Objectives

When you have completed the work in this chapter you should be able to:

1 Describe methods of measuring forces using the deformation of materials (e.g. extension and compression of springs).

2 Recall the theory explaining the origin of the normal contact force (reaction force) between surfaces.

3 Recall the theory which explains the origin of frictional forces between surfaces and explain qualitatively how frictional forces depend on the nature of the surface and the normal contact force.

4 Describe methods of recording the motion of a body, using ticker timers, stroboscopic techniques, and electrically controlled timers.

5 Analyse records of the motion of bodies and calculate from them displacements, velocities and accelerations.

Experiments in chapter 1

There are no experiments in chapter 1.

References

Akrill	Chapters 1, 2, 6
Duncan MM	Chapters 2, 6
Nelkon	Chapter 1
Wenham	Chapter 4
Whelan	Chapters 1, 2, 3
Williams	Chapters 2, 4, 5, 10

Chapter 1

Study time: 1 week

1.1 Introduction to forces

If you have not yet read the section 'How to use this student's guide' you should do so now.

If you were standing in a lunch queue and you suddenly went sprawling, you would probably get up angrily and look for whatever it was that had sent you flying. You would certainly know that you had been acted on by a force! This situation illustrates the four main aspects of what we mean in physics by a force.

1 You can *feel* a force (in this case painfully) as a push or a pull.

2 A force can *change the motion* of an object (in this case you were thrown on to the floor).

3 Force has *direction*, that is, it is a vector quantity. (In this case, if you sprawled forward you would conclude you were pushed or pulled forwards).

4 A force is the result of an *interaction* between two objects (in this case you would look for someone or something that had knocked you over). We shall see that a pair of forces always results from such an interaction.

We shall be developing these ideas of force – its nature, its causes and its effects – in this unit.

1.2 Measuring forces

Before we can go much further in our study of forces we must find some observable effect of a force which will provide a way of measuring the force.

Try this development question. This question helps you to develop a line of thought or argument by a series of short easy steps. Think about each part of the question before you look at the answers which follow.

Q **1.1 Development question**

(a) If you kick a football does the force of the kick change the ball's motion?

(b) Does the shape of the football change?

(c) If you kick a wall, will the force you exert move the wall? What is likely to happen to the wall?

(d) Does the football exert a force on the kicker? Does the wall? If so, suggest what is the origin of this force in each case. ■

Answers

(a) Yes, we change the direction of the ball and possibly its speed by the force we apply.

(b) The ball does get squashed out of shape by the force of the kick.

(c) You are unlikely to move the whole wall but, surprisingly, part of the wall will be set in motion by your force and will be squashed – just a little!

(d) You will certainly feel the force exerted by the wall on your foot and this force acts because the molecules of the wall are compressed (pushed closer together). Repulsive forces between the molecules oppose this compression, and the molecules exert a force on the body causing the compression – your foot. Of course, your toe also gets compressed which is why you feel the force of the wall! The compressed air inside the squashed football provides a similar force acting on your foot. (Development questions will not normally be followed by answers. Sometimes a suggested answer may be given at the back of the unit, but usually answers will be incorporated in the following text.)

Forces bend, squeeze and stretch things and the body they act on gets squeezed or stretched just enough to enable the many intermolecular forces to provide a resultant force which can balance the stretching (deforming) force. This idea provides a clue to the way we can measure force.

Q **1.2 Development question**

(a) What instrument is used for measuring force in the school laboratory?

(b) What is assumed in calibrating it? ■

We use the idea that a spring can be extended by a pull (or compressed by a push). When the spring is stretched by a certain stated amount, we conclude that a unit of force is pulling on each end (figure 1.1). If the spring is stretched twice this amount we conclude that we have two units of force.

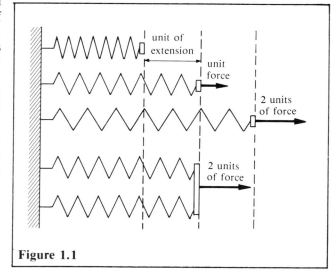

unit of extension

unit force

2 units of force

2 units of force

Figure 1.1

Q 1.3 Development question

(a) How do we know that two units of force produce twice as much stretch as one unit?
(b) How do we decide on a unit of force? ∎

It is a fortunate chance that for many springs *Hooke's law* can be applied. This states that the extension of a spring is proportional to the load (or force). We should note, though, that this law is not true for all springs. If Hooke's law did not hold we would have to use two identical springs stretched by unit extension to get two units of force (figure 1.1).

Clearly we must all use the same unit of force. This could be a force which produced the same stretch in identical springs. We could call this force one 'sprang' and define a 'standard stretched spring' as we define a standard mass of one kilogram. Defined in this way our unit would be an arbitrary fresh start – a *basic* unit not linked by this definition with any other units.

In choosing a system of units it is best to have as few basic units as possible and derive all other units from these. In the SI system of units the basic units are those which measure mass, length, time, electric current, temperature, amount of substance and luminous intensity. All other units can be derived from these. So the unit of force which is most appropriate is one which can be derived from the units of mass, length and time. In chapter 2 the *newton* will be defined in this way.

Q 1.4 Self-assessment question

Divide the list of units given below into basic units and derived units:
ampere, newton, kilogram, joule, watt, second, volt, kelvin. ∎

Note. A self-assessment question is intended to help you to check your progress. You should be able to work through such a question quickly and get it right – without looking at the answer first! The answers to all self-assessment questions are given at the back of the book, so that you can confirm your answer after you have done the question.

1.3 Types of force

In our study of mechanics we shall be dealing with two kinds of force:
(a) gravitational forces between masses, which are very weak and can be ignored unless we are near to a massive body like the earth;
(b) electromagnetic forces which produce intermolecular attractions and repulsions. These are responsible for most of the forces we consider, such as forces exerted by stretched springs, frictional forces, upthrusts due to displaced fluids, forces between charged bodies, between electric currents and between magnetised materials. (Two other types of force exist but they act only within the nucleus. They will be considered in the unit *Electrons and the nucleus.*)

Q 1.5 Study question

'Tension is not a force but a condition of a body acted upon by equal and opposite forces.' Explain this statement and suggest a reason why these forces act when a material is in tension. ∎

Using references in answering a study question

References are given at the beginning of each chapter. Some are to basic text books which cover a general topic like mechanics, some may be to books on very specific topics like gravity or friction. In all the references given you will find parts which are not relevant to a particular question. There are two ways of dealing with this efficiently.

1 Use the *index*. It is important to choose the *key words* from the question. In question 1.5, for example, a key word is 'tension' and you will find index references to this in several books. Reading more than one explanation will help your understanding.

2 Use *sub-headings* to find relevant sections of the chapters. Skim quickly through these sections and make brief notes of the points you want to include in your answer.

For more help on how to make notes, consult the APPIL *Student's Handbook* and read the relevant chapter in *Use your head* by Tony Buzan.

1.6 Study question

Q Figure 1.2 shows highly magnified sectional views across a piece of steel sliding over a copper plate; (b) is a later view of (a). Write a brief account of the modern view of the cause or origin of frictional forces. Show how this theory explains why friction is greatly reduced if:

(a) a lubricating oil is used,

(b) one of the surfaces is a soft material, e.g. the white metal bearings used in motor-car engines,

(c) material is used whose atoms are so strongly joined to one another that they do not easily join up with other atoms, e.g. polytetrafluorethylene (PTFE) used for non-stick pans and for the best skis. ■

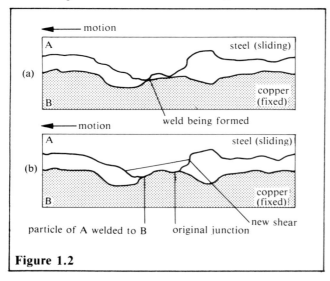

Figure 1.2

1.4 Analysing motion

How can we measure motion? We can measure the average speed of a body by timing it over a measured distance, but if we want to know everything about its motion (how it accelerates, when it reaches its maximum speed, etc.) we would have to know its position at every interval of time. We can usually get enough information by locating its position at very frequent intervals, and that is the principle used in analysing motion by ticker timers, stroboscopic photographs, cine films and radar scanners.

1.7 Study question

Q Find out what methods are employed for measuring and analysing motion. Outline briefly a suitable experimental method for finding each of the following (use a different method in each case).

(a) The average speed of the London–Edinburgh express.

(b) The constant acceleration of a steel ball falling in air.

(c) The speed of a cricket ball as it leaves the bowler's hand.

(d) The distance from the start at which a 100 m sprinter reaches his maximum speed.

(e) The approach speed of an aircraft just before landing. ■

In experiment FM 1 in chapter 2 you will need to calculate acceleration from the distance travelled by a body. First try the reverse process, calculating stopping distance from a car's deceleration.

Two factors determine stopping distance for a car:

(a) the distance travelled during the driver's reaction time (thinking distance),

(b) the distance travelled while the car is braking.

Assume that in (a) the car has a constant speed, and that in (b) it has a constant negative acceleration (slowing down steadily). The equation $v^2 - u^2 = 2as$ is applicable, where u and v are the initial and final velocities respectively, s is the distance travelled and a is the acceleration.

Note. Throughout this book the index system of notation is used for units. For example, the unit of velocity is metre per second, which is written as m s^{-1}. Similarly, the unit of acceleration is m s^{-2}.

1.8 Self-assessment question

Q (a) Assuming the reaction time is 0.7 s and $a = -7.5$ m s^{-2}, complete the table below.

initial speed	thinking distance	braking distance	total (stopping) distance
10 m s^{-1}			
20 m s^{-1}			
30 m s^{-1}			

(b) Compare your results with Highway Code data, assuming 20 m s^{-1} = 45 miles per hour. ■

Q 1.9 Self-assessment question

Figure 1.3 is a multiflash photograph of two golf balls, one projected horizontally at the same instant as the other begins falling vertically. An image of the ball was obtained on the photograph every time the stroboscopic lamp flashed and the interval between flashes was 1/30 s. The strings shown across the picture are 15 cm apart.

(a) Choose one clear image of the vertically falling ball, near to the beginning of its fall, and make this the start of your measurements of time and distance. Record the distances travelled in the next eight successive intervals of 1/30 second.

(b) Calculate the average velocity of the ball during each of these intervals.

(c) Draw a graph of average velocity against time measured from the instant when the ball was in the position you selected in part (a).

(d) Is the acceleration of the ball constant? Calculate the acceleration.

(e) For the ball which is projected horizontally, calculate its horizontal velocity and say whether this is constant.

(f) Does each ball have the same vertical acceleration? Give a reason for your answer.

(g) Assuming errors in timing are negligible, estimate the percentage errors in (i) measuring vertical distances, (ii) the calculated values of vertical velocities, and (iii) the calculated value of vertical acceleration. (To help you in answering this part of the question, refer to the Student's Handbook for a discussion of estimating errors.) ■

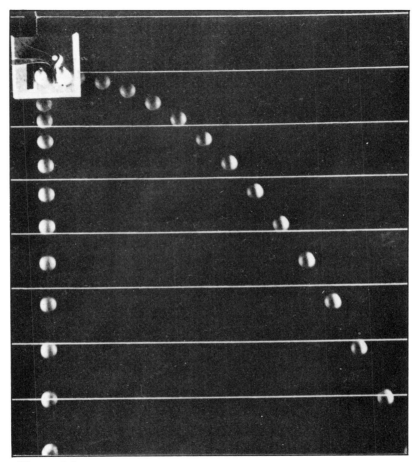

Figure 1.3

Acceleration at constant speed.

If a body changes the direction of its motion its velocity will change even when it is travelling at constant speed. Suppose a body is travelling with speed v_A when it is at point A (figure 1.4a), and after a short interval of time Δt it is at B and travelling with the same speed but in a direction making an angle θ with its direction of motion at A.

The average acceleration, a, between A and B is

$$\frac{\text{velocity at B} - \text{velocity at A}}{\text{time } \Delta t}$$

or $\quad a = \dfrac{v_B - v_A}{\Delta t}$

v_A and v_B are vectors and the quantity $v_B - v_A$ can be found by drawing a vector diagram. The quantity $v_B - v_A$ is the resultant of two vectors, v_B and $-v_A$, and $-v_A$ is a vector equal and opposite to v_A.

In figure 1.4 b PR represents the change in velocity $v_B - v_A$. This method will be used in chapter 4 when we consider the acceleration of bodies moving in a circle. As a foretaste of that chapter try the following question.

Q **1.10 Self-assessment question**
A car travels in a circular track of radius 100 m at a constant speed of 20 m s^{-1}. Find the size and direction of its *average acceleration* between two points from which the radii make an angle with each other of:
(a) 90°,
(b) 10°. ■

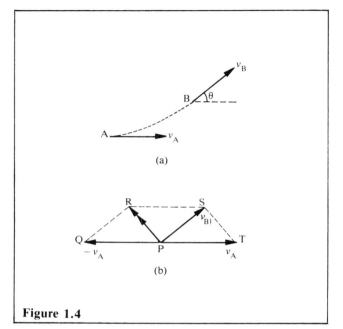

(a)

(b)

Figure 1.4

Summary
Equations for uniformly accelerated linear motion
$v = u + at$
$s = \dfrac{u + v}{2} t$
$s = ut + \frac{1}{2} at^2$
$v^2 = u^2 + 2as$

Questions on objectives

Before you attempt these, check through the list of objectives for this chapter and make sure that your notes on the chapter have not left out anything important.

1 Estimate, for your journey from home to school,
(a) your average speed,
(b) your average velocity.
Indicate by a sketch or in some other way what quantities you use to make these estimates and explain why they may differ.

(objective 4)

2 An experiment is planned to determine a value for the gravitational acceleration *g* by projecting a sphere vertically upwards and measuring the maximum height reached and the time taken for the sphere to return to the point of projection. Suggest what apparatus might be required, outline the steps in the procedure to be adopted, and explain how the observations would be used to obtain a result.

(objective 4)

3 A tile slides off a roof inclined at an angle of 30° to the horizontal at a speed of 4 ms⁻¹.
(a) What are the horizontal and vertical components of its velocity when it leaves the roof?
(b) How long does it take to reach the ground 20m below?
(c) At what horizontal distance from the building does it land?

(objective 5)

4 Figure 1.5 shows the velocity–time curve for a *light* object thrown vertically upwards.
(a) Describe the motion and suggest what the light object might be made of.
(b) Estimate the height to which the object rises above the point of projection.
(c) How do you know from the graph that the object returned to the projection point?
(d) Estimate the accelerations at point A and at point B.

(objective 5)

Compare the time you took to complete this chapter with the recommended time. Are you keeping up to schedule?

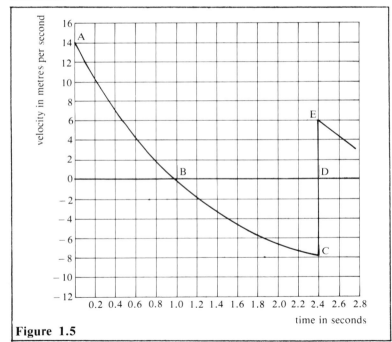

Figure 1.5

Chapter 2

Aim

In this chapter you will study Newton's laws of motion. You will observe the motion of bodies under the influence of forces, and explain your observations using Newton's laws. You will then apply this knowledge to a system of interacting bodies, and finally consider the limitations of Newton's laws when applied to systems travelling at high speeds.

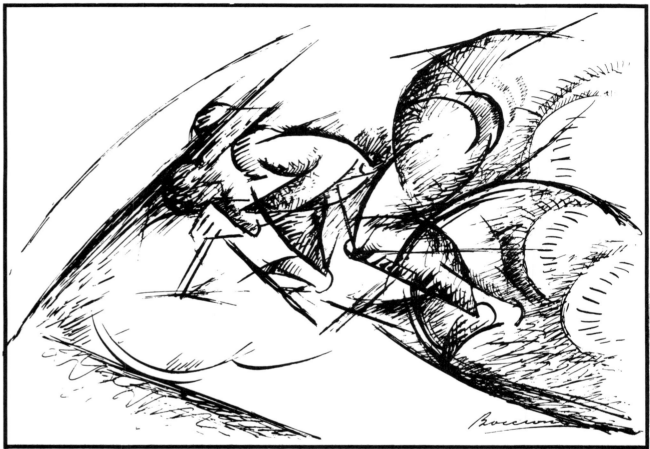

Dynamics of a cyclist

Objectives

When you have completed the work in this chapter you should be able to:

1 Use the following scientific terms correctly: momentum, inertia, inertial mass, weight, gravitational mass, system (of interacting bodies).

2 Define the term momentum, and state the SI unit in which it is measured.

3 State the dimensions of force and define the unit of force – the newton.

4 State, in words and mathematical symbols, Newton's three laws of motion.

5 Apply Newton's laws of motion to explain and predict the behaviour of bodies acted on by external forces.

6 Solve numerical problems involving Newton's laws of motion.

7 Investigate experimentally the relationship between force, mass and acceleration.

8 Identify situations in which Newton's laws are not applicable.

Experiments in chapter 2

FM 1 Motion due to a steady force
(1 hour)

References

Akrill	Chapters 5 and 6
Bolton	Chapter 2
Duncan MM	Chapter 6
Nelkon	Chapter 1
Thorning	Chapters 2 and 4
Wenham	Chapters 5 and 6
Whelan	Chapter 3
Williams	Chapters 4 and 5

Chapter

2

Study time: 1 week

2.1 Force and inertia

In 1687, Isaac Newton published a book which is regarded as one of the greatest scientific works ever written. It was called *Philosophiae Naturalis Principia Mathematica* which translates to 'The mathematical principles of natural philosophy'. These principles concerned the motion of objects, and Newton summed up the connection between the motion of any object and the resultant force on it in three laws.

These can be stated in a number of ways, so don't worry if the statements of the laws given in this chapter are not word for word the same as you may have read elsewhere, but satisfy yourself that they mean exactly the same thing.

The idea of *inertia* is one which eluded scientists for many centuries because they were convinced, wrongly, that forces were needed to sustain motion. Aristotle thought that a moving body comes to a standstill when the forces pushing it no longer act. It was not until science became truly experimental that the breakthrough came. Galileo's experiments in 1638, timing the motion of rolling balls on inclined tracks, led him to predict that motion along a perfectly smooth horizontal track would be steady and perpetual. So he developed his idea of inertia, which is embodied in Newton's first law.

Law 1 Unless a resultant force acts on a body its velocity will not change.

This simple statement about the meaning of force has been described as one of the great breakthroughs in scientific thought. The law states that forces produce *change* in motion, and that bodies have the property of resistance to changes in their motion or state of rest. This property is called inertia.

Background reading

For an exciting account of the work of Galileo and Newton, read Koestler, A. *The sleepwalkers.*

Q 2.1 Self-assessment question
(a) When a car is travelling along a horizontal road the engine must be kept running, applying a force to turn the wheels, if the car is to be kept going at constant speed. This seems to contradict Newton's first law. Explain why you think the law is applicable in this case.
(b) How does the idea of inertia suggest what may happen to the passengers if the brake is applied suddenly? ■

Inertial mass

How do we define mass? Newton described it as 'quantity of matter' and that is how we first think of mass, by describing it using other words like 'matter' or 'stuff'. This doesn't help us too much until we clearly define what we mean by *quantity*. It isn't volume, and it isn't number of atoms. But we can say that the inertia of a body – the way it resists changes when forces act – depends on 'the quantity or amount of matter' and we can use the phrase 'inertial mass' to describe mass with reference to its key property of inertia.

Q 2.2 Self-assessment question
Two closed tins are suspended from the ceiling on string. One is empty, the other full of sand. How could you identify the empty one? ■

Q 2.3 Study question
The unit of mass is the kilogram.
(a) How is this unit defined?
(b) How is mass measured? ■

Q 2.4 Self-assessment question*

A large mass (1 kg or more) is suspended by a thread A from a rigid support and a similar thread B is attached to the bottom of the mass (figure 2.1). Use the idea of inertia to predict and explain what will happen if you pull the lower thread B
(a) sharply,
(b) steadily.
(Think how different parts will respond to the pull. When you have written your answer you could try the experiment.) ∎

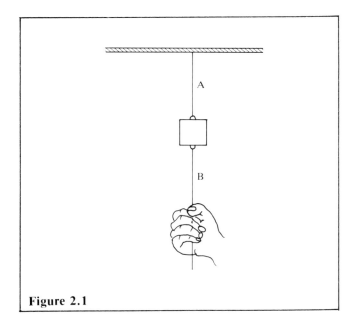

Figure 2.1

Q 2.5 Self-assessment question

Figure 2.2 shows what happens to a pile of wooden blocks when one of them is given a sharp knock.
(a) Are there any forces on the other blocks when one of them is hit?
(b) Why have the other blocks not moved?
(c) What would happen if the block next to the top one was hit?
(Test your theories by pulling out one book from a pile of text books. Try pulling one near the bottom of the pile, and then one near the top.) ∎

Q 2.6 Self-assessment question

(a) Why is it dangerous to step off a moving train on to a platform?
(b) Explain why an umbrella can be dried by turning it upside down and rapidly closing and opening it. ∎

Q 2.7 Self-assessment question

Ships take much longer than cars to slow down. Suggest *two* reasons for this. ∎

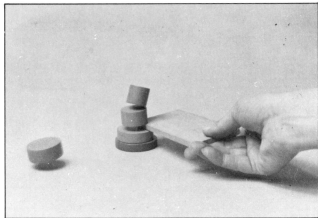

Figure 2.2

2.2 Force, acceleration and mass

What happens when a steady force is applied to a body? This time, instead of beginning with Newton's axiom, obtain some evidence from your own experiment about the kind of motion produced.

E Experiment FM 1
Motion due to a steady force

In this experiment you will investigate how the acceleration of a body of fixed mass depends on the applied force, and how the same force produces different accelerations for bodies of different masses.

Law 2 The rate of change of momentum of a body is proportional to the resultant force acting, and occurs in the direction in which the force is acting.

This law describes the kind of motion produced by a resultant force. Law 1 can be thought of as a special case (no force, and so no change in motion) of this more general law. Newton used the word 'motion' instead of momentum in his original statement but this was confusing, because people used the phrase 'quantity of motion' to mean both momentum and motion energy (kinetic energy). It is very important to know exactly what we mean by the word 'momentum'. It is defined as

$$\text{momentum} = \text{mass} \times \text{velocity}$$
$$\text{or} \qquad p = mv$$

where p is the momentum, m is the mass and v is the velocity. Momentum is measured in units of kg m s^{-1} or N s. Note that, since velocity is a vector quantity and mass is a scalar quantity, momentum is a vector quantity.

Q **2.8 Development question**
A constant force F acts on a body of mass m for time t, and produces a change in velocity from u to v.
(a) Write down an expression for the change of momentum p.
(b) Write down an expression for the *rate* of change of momentum.
(c) Now write an expression for the acceleration a.
(d) Write down an expression for Newton's second law using your answers to (a) and (b).
(e) Use your answers to (c) and (d) to show that $F = kma$, where k is a constant. ■

This equation is true for a body of constant mass acted on by a constant force, but remember that Newton's law holds for all cases, even when the force is variable and the mass is changing. So this equation expresses Newton's second law even if F, m and a are all varying. Remember that since force and acceleration are two vector quantities, the equation expresses the fact that the direction of the force is also the direction of the acceleration and the momentum change.

Another way of stating the law is

$$F \propto \frac{\Delta(mv)}{\Delta t}$$

when $\Delta(mv)$ is the change in momentum occurring in a small time Δt.

Using calculus notation

$$F \propto \frac{\mathrm{d}}{\mathrm{d}t}(mv).$$

If the mass m is constant,

then $\qquad F \propto m \dfrac{\mathrm{d}v}{\mathrm{d}t}$

or $\qquad F \propto ma$

AV **FM 4 Film loop**
Newton's first and second laws
This film loop shows you how these laws can be investigated through measurements of almost frictionless motion on an air-track.

The newton

In experiment FM1, arbitrary units of force (the pull of one stretched elastic cord) and of mass (a trolley) were used.

Newton's second law provides a means of defining a unit of force, derived from the basic units kilogram, metre and second, from the equation $F = kma$.

The constant k is made equal to 1 by defining a unit of force, the newton (N), so that if m is in kg, a in m s^{-2} and F in N, then

➡ $\qquad F = ma$

Q **2.9 Self-assessment question**
Use the equation above to write a definition of the newton in words. ■

Q **2.10 Study question**
(a) What is meant by the *dimensions* of a physical quantity?
(b) What are the dimensions of force? ■

You can get an idea of the size of a newton by considering a falling body. All bodies allowed to fall freely on earth have an acceleration of approximately 9.8 m s^{-2} (it is approximate because it varies slightly from place to place on the earth). For many purposes we can use the value 10.0 m s^{-2}, which is within 2% of the true value. We can use the equation $F = ma$ to work out the force producing this acceleration.

An average-sized apple has a mass of 0.1 kg so the force on this apple = 0.1 kg × 10 m s^{-2} = 1 N. This is an amusing coincidence, considering the part an apple is supposed to have played in developing Isaac Newton's ideas!

Q 2.11 Self-assessment question

Figure 2.3 is a stroboscopic photograph of two objects falling under gravity. Use the photograph to calculate the acceleration due to gravity. The flashing rate of the stroboscope and the scale are given. What can you say about the ratio of the forces acting on these two bodies? ∎

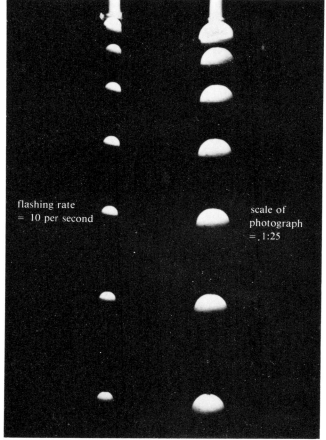

flashing rate
= 10 per second

scale of
photograph
= 1:25

Figure 2.3

Weight

The weight of a body is the pull of the earth acting on the body. This pull acts towards the centre of the earth. The earth produces a gravitational field, and a force acts on all bodies in such a field. This force is proportional to the mass of the body. The strength of the gravitational field is measured in newtons per kilogram, $N\,kg^{-1}$. The mass referred to here is called the gravitational mass, since it determines the gravitational force acting on the body. In the equation $F = ma$, the mass m was the inertial mass of a body. However, gravitational mass and inertial mass are found to be equivalent (masses with the same weight always have the same inertia) so we don't normally distinguish between them. In general, a mass m placed in a region where the acceleration due to gravity is g has a weight mg. Thus $F = ma$ is rewritten $W = mg$ where W is in newtons, m in kilograms and g in metres per second squared or newtons per kilogram.

The force acting on a support is sometimes called 'the weight'. Bathroom scales record this force. You feel your weight by experiencing an upward force acting on your body to support you. Such forces may disappear. If you were standing on a set of scales in a freely falling lift, the scales would record zero. You wouldn't feel any weight on your feet and the state would be described as 'weightlessness', though, of course, you would still have a weight – a force of gravity acting on you.

Q 2.12 Study question

Two instruments are commonly used to weigh objects: spring balances and lever-type balances. Which of these is not really measuring weight? Explain why not. ∎

Q 2.13 Self-assessment question

Predict how the 'weight' of an astronaut will vary as he travels from the earth in a rocket which moves into orbit round the earth. Distinguish between the changes in the pull of the earth on the astronaut (his weight) and what he actually feels. ∎

EXTENSION

Equivalence of gravitational and inertial mass.

You may have wondered why these two aspects of mass are the same. They arise from quite different ideas – an attraction between bodies, and the resistance of bodies to changes in motion. So how can they be equivalent? If they always are, does this tell us more about the nature of things? This was the question Einstein asked, and he developed his general theory of relativity in finding the answer. This is not in the A level syllabus, but it is an important part of physics. An account can be found in Rogers, E. M. *Physics for the inquiring mind*, pages 118 and 498. You can read this if you are interested in following this argument. It is one of a number of places where physics spills over into philosophy.

Solving problems
using Newton's second law

The equation $F = ma$ has an extremely wide application and is very useful in solving problems in mechanics. It should be noted that

(a) F is the *resultant* force in any situation, and

(b) a is the acceleration of the body in the direction of the resultant force.

You may find it helpful to follow the procedure outlined below.

1 Draw a diagram to represent the general situation, marking all the bodies involved.

2 Select from the situation the body whose motion is to be analysed. Draw a diagram of this body, with all the forces acting on it. Mark the size of each force in newtons, and show the direction of each force. (Do not mark the forces exerted by this body on other bodies, since they are not relevant.)

3 Select convenient axes, and mark the acceleration a in the direction to be considered.

4 Find the resultant force F and apply the law.

Q 2.14 Self-assessment question
A resultant force of 4.0 N is applied to a body of mass 2.0 kg for a time of 1.0 s.
(a) What is the acceleration of the body?
(b) If the body was initially at rest, how far would it travel during the time the force is applied? ■

Q 2.15 Self-assessment question
Forces of 15 N and 20 N act on a body of mass 5.0 kg. If the forces are perpendicular to each other, calculate the magnitude and direction of the acceleration of the body. ■

Q 2.16 Self-assessment question
A lift has a mass of 1.5×10^3 kg. Calculate the tension in the supporting cable when the lift is
(a) descending at uniform velocity,
(b) descending with downward acceleration 2.0 m s^{-2},
(c) at rest,
(d) ascending with upward acceleration 2.0 m s^{-2},
(e) ascending at uniform velocity.
(Assume $g = 10.0$ m s^{-2}) ■

Q 2.17 Self-assessment question
When a jet aircraft is launched from an aircraft carrier, its horizontal speed is increased from 0 to 60 m s^{-1} in about 5 s.
(a) What horizontal acceleration is experienced by the pilot?
(b) If the pilot has a mass of 80 kg, estimate the magnitude and direction of the force exerted on him by the pilot seat during launching.
(Assume $g = 10$ m s^{-2}) ■

Q 2.18 Self-assessment question
Sketch displacement–time and velocity–time graphs to represent each of the following motions.
(a) A puck on a frictionless incline of constant slope is given a sharp push up the incline and eventually returns to its starting point.
(b) A driver accelerates his car as quickly as possible from rest, through three gear changes, to 30 m s^{-1}.
(c) A stone is released from a stationary balloon about 1 km above the earth's surface. Frictional forces oppose the motion of the stone. These forces increase steadily as the velocity increases, until they are eventually equal in magnitude to the gravitational force acting on the stone. The stone hits the ground and is brought rapidly to rest by soft, wet sand. ■

Q 2.19 Self-assessment question
A boy of mass 60 kg jumps from a wall 1.25 m high on to a hard playground, but forgets to bend his knees while landing. The total 'give' is only 2.5 cm in compression of the ground and the boy's feet, ankles, etc. during the stopping process.
(Use $g = 10$ m s^{-2})
(a) How long does he take in falling from the wall to the ground?
(b) What is his speed at the end of the fall?
(c) Calculate the acceleration during landing. (Assume that the resisting force is constant.)
(d) What is the final upward force exerted by the ground on the boy after he has stopped moving?
(e) Is this force in existence throughout the landing process?
(f) Calculate the total force exerted by the ground on the boy during landing.
(g) If the boy bends his knees during landing so that his body is brought to rest smoothly in a time of 100 ms, what force is exerted by the ground during landing?
(h) How far does the centre of mass of his body travel during the landing process if he bends his knees? ▨

2.3 Interactions

Law 3 If a body A exerts a force on body B, then body B will exert an equal and opposite force on body A.

This expresses the idea that a force always involves two bodies. For example, if you step off a skateboard, the skateboard will move in the opposite direction to you. You have used the force exerted by the skateboard on you to move forwards. Simultaneously, you have exerted an equal force on the skateboard to propel it in the opposite direction. Figure 2.4 illustrates a marine version of this situation!

The third law is often stated in the form 'action and reaction are equal and opposite', but this statement can lead to misunderstanding. It does not emphasise that the 'third-law pair' of forces act on two different bodies. Also, it is not possible to distinguish from the effects of these forces which is the 'action' and which the 'reaction': both are interaction forces.

Even when one interacting body is much larger than the other, the law is still true although its effect is less obvious. If you drop a book, the force of the earth on the book is obvious from its acceleration. But the earth is being pulled up by the book with an equal and opposite force, though the earth's movement cannot be detected. We call this a gravitational force pair (figure 2.5).

Figure 2.4   The perils of Newton's third law

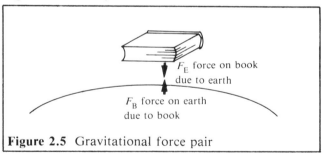

F_E force on book due to earth

F_B force on earth due to book

Figure 2.5 Gravitational force pair

Newton's third law applies in every case, whether the bodies are in equilibrium or accelerating. If the book is resting on a table there will be another 'third-law pair' of forces. The matter in both bodies will be compressed and forces of interatomic repulsion will produce a 'third-law pair' – the book pushing down on the table and the table pushing up on the book (figure 2.6). These interatomic repulsion forces will always be equal and opposite to each other, but not necessarily equal to the weight of the book. For example, if the book was placed on a pile of cotton wool an interatomic force pair would act immediately, but the book would accelerate downwards.

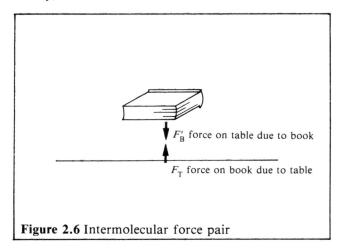

F'_B force on table due to book

F_T force on book due to table

Figure 2.6 Intermolecular force pair

What forces are acting on the book when it is on a table? Two of the four forces shown in figures 2.5 and 2.6 act on the book, as shown in figure 2.7. These forces are the gravitational pull of the earth and the force due to compression of the table matter (called the *reaction* force). These two forces may or may not be equal, but if they are equal then remember that it is because of the strength of the table and has nothing to do with Newton's third law.

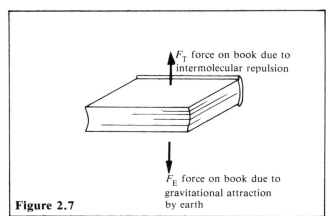

F_T force on book due to intermolecular repulsion

F_E force on book due to gravitational attraction by earth

Figure 2.7

Q **2.20 Self-assessment question**
For each of the following situations, draw a force diagram of all the forces acting on each body mentioned. Then, remembering that each force you have indicated is part of a 'third-law pair', list these pairs.
(a) A stone falling freely to earth in a vacuum (1 pair).
(b) A car travelling along a horizontal road (3 pairs).
(c) Two men engaged in a tug-of-war with a rope (6 pairs). ∎

Q **2.21 Self-assessment question**
'Frictional forces always act in pairs.' Explain this statement, and discuss why friction is vital if you want to walk. What would be the result of screwing a nut on to a bolt if there was no friction between the two surfaces in contact? ∎

Q **2.22 Study question**
To become familiar with the way in which Newton's three laws are useful in solving problems, look through several numerical questions in one of the references given at the beginning of this chapter, and plan how you would solve the problems, noting how the different laws are used. Do not do any calculations. It is more important to learn how to tackle a variety of problems than to obtain a lot of answers to similar problems. ∎

AV **FM 5 Film loop**
Newton's third law
This loop demonstrates the third law in action, using a frictionless air-track.

Limitations of Newton's laws of motion
These three important laws form the basis of dynamics but, like all laws, they have their limitations. In particular, the laws do not correctly predict the behaviour of the following.
(a) Bodies moving with very high speeds, approaching that of light. (In these cases the modifications of the special theory of relativity are required.)
(b) Bodies with very small masses, approaching that of the proton. (In these cases the modifications of the quantum theory are required.)

In most of our experience we are concerned with objects much more massive than a proton, travelling considerably slower than the speed of light. So, in most circumstances, Newton's laws are very accurate predictors of the way bodies move. The computers used to control space vehicles are programmed using Newton's laws, and the accuracy of space missions is testimony to the wide validity of Newtonian mechanics.

Questions on objectives

1 State the dimensions of force and show how these are derived.

(objective 3)

2 How could an astronaut on the moon measure
(a) mass, and
(b) weight?

(objectives 1 and 5)

3 A stone hangs stationary from a spring balance which reads 9.8 N.
(a) What forces act on the stone? What can you say about the resultant of these forces?
(b) The thread holding the stone breaks and it falls. What force acts on it while it is falling? How do you know that this force is acting?
(c) What is the mass of the stone? Why is this an approximate value, even if we assume the balance is accurate?
(d) A pebble of mass 102 g rests on your hand. If the acceleration due to gravity is 9.80 m s⁻², what is the size of the force you are providing to support it?

(objectives 1 and 6)

4 A stalled car is being pushed along a level road. Its speed is increased from rest to 3.0 m s⁻¹ in 6.0 s. If the mass of the car is 660 kg, what is the average resultant force needed to give the car this acceleration? If there is a frictional force of 100 N acting during this time, what total force must be applied to the car?

(objective 6)

5 A trolley of mass 4.0 kg has free-running wheels and is originally at rest on a horizontal surface (figure 2.8). It is connected by a light rope passing over a well-oiled pulley to a block of mass 1.0 kg.
(a) Write two equations, one for the trolley and one for the block, relating the forces acting on them to their acceleration.
(b) Calculate the acceleration of the two masses (assume $g = 10$ ms⁻²).
(c) What is the tension force in the rope?
(d) What is the speed of the trolley when it has travelled 2.0 m?

(objective 6)

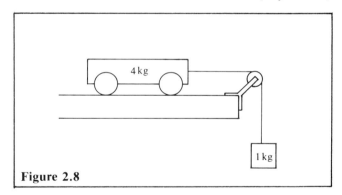

Figure 2.8

6 A car of mass 1000 kg, travelling in a straight line at 15 m s⁻¹, is retarded by a constant force when its brakes are applied and comes to rest in a distance of 60 m. Find the magnitude of the retarding force and the time for which it acts.

(objectives 5 and 6)

7 If a parachutist is descending at constant velocity with his parachute open, Dick argues that the parachutist's weight is balanced by an equal and opposite force due to air resistance and so he experiences no acceleration. Tom agrees and adds that the two forces are an example of Newton's third law, which says that forces always act in equal and opposite pairs.
(a) Do you agree with Dick, or Tom, or both? Why?
(b) Name four more forces involved in this situation and arrange all the six forces into three 'third-law pairs.'

(objectives 1 and 5)

Chapter 3

Aim

In this chapter you will study collisions, and consider the momentum and energy changes occurring within a system of interacting bodies. You will also examine evidence in support of the principles of conservation of momentum and energy. The results of this study will be applied to the principles of powered flight, and of safety design in cars.

Objectives

When you have completed the work in this chapter you should be able to:

1 Use the following scientific terms correctly: impulse, elastic collision, inelastic collision, system (of interacting bodies), isolated closed system, inertial frame of reference.

2 Define the following quantity, giving the correct unit: impulse.

3 State, in words and in mathematical symbols,
(a) the principle of conservation of momentum,
(b) the principle of conservation of energy.

4 Solve problems involving the interactions of bodies, in one dimension, using the above principles.

5 EXTENSION
Solve problems involving the interactions of bodies in two dimensions.

6 Describe experiments to verify
(a) the principle of conservation of linear momentum,
(b) the principle of conservation of energy, during a transfer of kinetic energy to potential energy.

7 Estimate the limits of accuracy in the experiments you carry out.

Experiments in chapter 3

FM 2 Conservation of momentum
(1 hour)
FM 3 Energy and momentum changes
($\frac{3}{4}$ hour)
FM 4 The speed of a rifle bullet
($\frac{1}{2}$ hour)
FM 5 A multiple collision – Newton's cradle
($\frac{1}{2}$ hour)

References

Akrill	Chapters 7, 8, 9
Bolton	Chapters 2, 3
Duncan MM	Chapter 6
Nelkon	Chapter 1
Thorning	Chapter 3
Wenham	Chapters 5, 7, 8
Whelan	Chapters 4, 5
Williams	Chapters 8, 9

Chapter

3

Study time: 2 weeks

3.1 Momentum and impulse

Q 3.1 Development question
(a) Write the equation of Newton's second law for a case in which a force F, acting for a time t on a body of mass m, increases its velocity from u to v.
(b) Rearrange this equation to express the change of momentum in terms of F. ■

The quantity Ft is called the *impulse* of the force on the body. Thus
impulse = change of momentum.
Impulse, like momentum, is a vector quantity, and both have the same unit.

When a force acts for a very short time as, for example, when two bodies collide or a football is kicked, the force producing the change in momentum is rarely constant. A graph of force against time when a football is kicked would look something like figure 3.1.

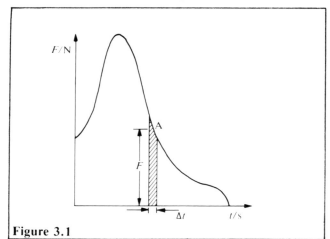

Figure 3.1

The change in momentum produced in a short time Δt must be equal to the product $F \Delta t$ (represented by the shaded strip). The whole area under the curve represents the total change in momentum, which is equal to the impulse. Expressing Newton's second law in calculus notation,

$$F = \frac{\mathrm{d}}{\mathrm{d}t} (mv)$$

or, writing p instead of mv for momentum,

$$F = \frac{\mathrm{d}p}{\mathrm{d}t} .$$

Integrating this equation gives

$$\int_{t_1}^{t_2} F \,\mathrm{d}t = \int_{p_1}^{p_2} \mathrm{d}p$$
$$= p_2 - p_1$$
$$= m(v - u)$$

For a steady force, impulse = Ft

For a variable force, impulse = $\int_{t_1}^{t_2} F \,\mathrm{d}t$

To measure the impulse it is only necessary to know the change of momentum produced, and not how the force varies. Impulse is measured in units of newton second.

Q 3.2 Development question
(a) Write down the dimensions of velocity, momentum, force, and impulse. (Refer to the section on dimensions in the Student's Handbook.)
(b) Show that the units N s and kg m s^{-1} are equivalent. ■

Q 3.3 Self-assessment question
(a) Why can a nail be hammered into a block of wood when no amount of pushing will avail?
(b) What happens if you try hammering a nail into a plank which is resting on a piece of sponge rubber? Why? ■

Q 3.4 Self-assessment question
Use the equation $Ft = m(v - u)$ to explain the following.
(a) In making a good stroke in cricket·tennis or golf it is important to 'follow through' when hitting the ball.
(b) A fast moving cricket ball is more likely to be caught without discomfort if the hands are drawn back in the direction in which the ball is travelling.
(c) Eggs are less likely to break when dropped if they are in an expanded polystyrene container, rather than a hard plastic one. ■

3.2 Conservation of momentum

We will now look at a simple situation where momentum changes, namely a collision between two bodies. Figure 3.2 shows trolleys A and B of masses m_1 and m_2 and velocities u_1 and u_2 respectively. They are travelling in the same direction and for a collision clearly u_1 must be greater than u_2. During the collision A exerts a force F on B to the right. From Newton's third law, B must exert an equal and opposite force F on A. Of course, the force will vary during the collision but at any instant the force on A must be equal and opposite to the force on B. Both forces will act for the same length of time t and so the two bodies receive equal but opposite impulses. As a result of these impulses the velocities change to v_1 and v_2.

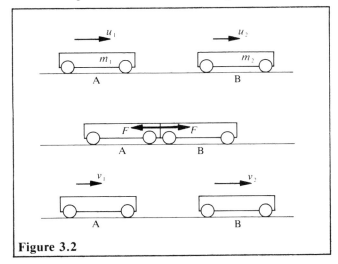

Figure 3.2

Q **3.5 Development question***
(a) Express in symbols the equation

$$\text{impulse on A of B} = \text{momentum of A after collision} - \text{momentum of A before collision}$$

writing all velocities and forces to the right as positive and those to the left as negative.
(b) Write a similar equation for trolley B.
(c) Hence show that the total momentum before collision is equal to the total momentum after collision. ∎

The answer to the last question is one way of expressing the *principle of conservation of momentum:* in an isolated or closed system of bodies the total momentum is unaffected by any interactions between the bodies.

Since momentum is a vector quantity, it is possible to consider one particular direction in a system of bodies. If there is no external force acting on the system in that direction, the total vector momentum in that direction remains constant, even if the bodies are acting on each other. Linear momentum is conserved. In cases where momentum along one line only is being considered, we can use a simple sign convention: momentum to the right is positive, momentum to the left is negative.

E **Experiment FM 2**
Conservation of momentum
In this experiment you will observe a number of different kinds of collisions, to collect empirical evidence in support of the principle of conservation of momentum.

Q **3.6 Self-assessment question**
Trolley B has a mass of 1.0 kg and is initially at rest. Trolley A comes towards B from the left with a velocity of 0.50 m s^{-1}, and the two trolleys link together on collision so that they move off together. Calculate the velocity after collision if the mass of A is
(a) 1.0 kg
(b) 2.0 kg ∎

Here we see one advantage of the conservation principle: it is not necessary to know how the force between the bodies varies during collision. Only the initial and final velocities are needed, and these are much easier to determine. Another advantage is that the principle has a very wide application, including all interactions between two or more bodies. Take, for example, an explosion of a gun firing a bullet. This results in forward momentum of the bullet p_B and backward momentum of the gun p_G. If the gun and bullet were both stationary before explosion we can write

$$p_B + p_G = 0$$

3.7 Self-assessment question

Q A gun of mass 1.5 kg fires a bullet of mass 5.0×10^{-2} kg with a muzzle velocity of 1.0×10^3 m s^{-1}.
(a) What is the initial momentum of the bullet?
(b) What is the initial momentum of the gun?
(c) What is the initial velocity of the gun's recoil? ■

In experiment FM 2 we were assuming that the systems we were observing were closed, or isolated, systems for which the conservation principle applied. What is a closed system?

A closed system must include all the bodies taking part in the interaction – in other words there can be no resultant external forces involved. In figure 3.3, trolley B cannot form a closed system, because when trolley A collides with it B is acted on by a repelling force due to the molecules of A, which is a force external to the system. Gravity is an external force, but we can exclude that if we are dealing only with horizontal interactions, and we shall have to assume no friction if we are leaving the 'ground' outside our system. Make sure when you apply the conservation of momentum principle that you are making your 'closed system' big enough. There are cases where at first sight it is difficult to see how momentum is conserved.

Take the example of a car coasting on a level road. It will eventually come to rest because of air resistance forces and frictional forces. The car's momentum has not been conserved, but the car on its own is not an isolated system. The car is interacting with the ground (by friction) and with the atmosphere, so the earth is part of the closed system.

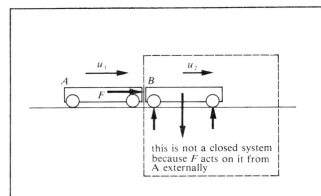

this is not a closed system because F acts on it from A externally

Figure 3.3

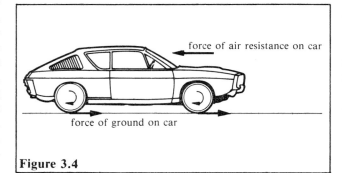

force of air resistance on car

force of ground on car

Figure 3.4

3.8 Self-assessment question

Q Figure 3.4 shows the horizontal forces acting on a coasting car.
(a) What horizontal forces act on other bodies as the car coasts along?
(b) What other external forces act on the car? ■

If the car moves forward, accelerating to velocity u_C, the earth's velocity will change by u_E in the opposite direction. The forward momentum acquired by the car will be balanced by an equal and opposite momentum acquired by the earth (which will be impossible to detect).

3.9 Self-assessment question

Q If the car slows down and eventually stops, will the earth's original motion be restored? Explain. ■

Investigating the conservation of momentum experimentally, it is necessary to eliminate or compensate for friction. Then it is not necessary to measure changes in the velocity of the earth, because we have arranged a closed system which does not include the earth.

The exchange of momentum between interacting bodies is easier to observe if the masses involved are of similar magnitude.

Q 3.10 Self-assessment question

A car of mass 1 kg stands on a trolley of mass 2 kg. The trolley is on wheels and able to move freely on a horizontal surface (figure 3.5). Initially both car and trolley are stationary, and points X on the car and Y on the trolley are vertically in line with a point Z on the runway. A spring in the car is then released, and this pushes a plunger against the stop at one end of the trolley as a result of which the car almost instantaneously acquires a steady speed of 0.2 m s⁻¹ with respect to Z. After three seconds it hits the other stop and remains in contact with it. Find
(a) the speed of Y with respect to Z before and after the car hits the stop,
(b) the positions of X and Y with respect to Z at the instant that the car comes to rest against the stop. ■

Q 3.11 Self-assessment question

Two rods are rigidly mounted on a freely-running trolley, and a heavy pendulum bob is suspended from the junction of the rods. The bob is tied to one rod by a cotton loop (see figure 3.6a).
The trolley is at rest on a horizontal surface and the cotton loop is burned through.
(a) Use the principle of the conservation of momentum to explain the subsequent motion of the trolley.
(b) The experiment is repeated with a lump of putty stuck on the trolley so that the bob strikes the putty and adheres to it at the lowest point of swing (see figure 3.6b). Explain what happens now.
(c) What would happen if the experiment is again repeated, this time with a rigid steel plate fixed to the trolley in place of the putty? ■

Q 3.12 Self-assessment question

Student A finds the conservation of momentum difficult to accept, because when he hurls a lump of plasticine at a brick wall its momentum disappears.
Student B says he believes in the conservation law, and suggests that by throwing a massive lump of plasticine in a westward direction to hit a brick wall he will slow down the earth's rotation and make the day longer.
Comment on these views and give your own. ■

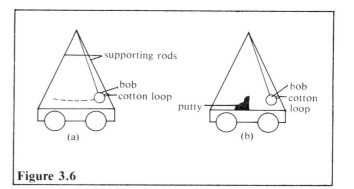

Figure 3.6

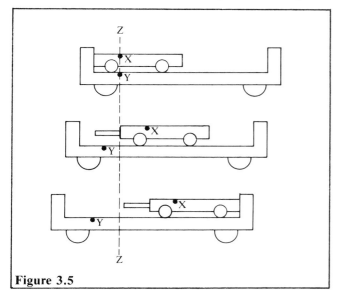

Figure 3.5

3.3 Energy changes

Energy is the capacity for doing work. Work is done when the point of application of a force moves in a direction along which there is some positive component of the force. Figure 3.7 indicates the work done when the point of application of a force moves from X to Y.

When work is done on a body, the body then has an increased capacity for doing work: its energy has increased.

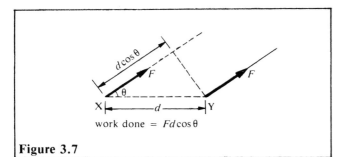

work done = $Fd\cos\theta$

Figure 3.7

Q **3.13 Development question**
A steady force F pushes a body mass m through a distance s in the direction of the force. The acceleration of the body is a and its velocity increases from zero to v.
(a) What is the work done by the force?
(b) Express F in terms of m and a.
(c) Express s in terms of v and a.
(d) Use your answers to (b) and (c) to derive an expression for the kinetic energy of the body.
(e) Write down the change in kinetic energy of the body if its speed decreases from v to u. ■

➡ The kinetic energy of a body mass m travelling with speed v is $\frac{1}{2}mv^2$

Q **3.14 Development question**
Figure 3.8 shows a body, mass m, lifted through a height h from A to B against the pull of the earth.
(a) What potential energy does it acquire when moved from A to B?
(b) If the body falls from B calculate its (i) velocity, (ii) potential energy, (iii) kinetic energy, (iv) total energy as it passes through point C, distance x below B.
(c) What can you say about the total mechanical energy which the body possesses at *any* point during its fall? (Assume that there is no change in the velocity or energy of the massive earth when the small mass m moves.) ■

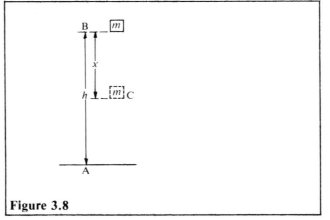

Figure 3.8

Work done by a variable force

Q **3.15 Development question***
Figure 3.9a shows a graph of a force which remains steady as its point of application is moved through distance d.
Figure 3.9b shows a graph for a variable force.
(a) What does the shaded area in figure 3.9a represent?
(b) What does the shaded strip in figure 3.9b represent?
(c) How can the work done by a variable force moving through distance d be calculated? ■

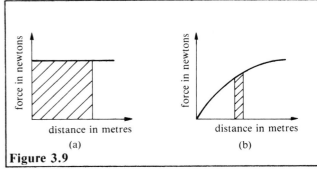

Figure 3.9

Q 3.16 Self-assessment question

An archery bow is drawn back using a force meter and the readings of force F and displacement d are listed below.

F/N	0	70	120	180	300	500
d/m	0	0.2	0.3	0.4	0.5	0.6

Plot a graph of force against displacement and find from it the energy stored in the fully drawn bow. Calculate
(a) the *initial* acceleration which a 400 g arrow would have when fired from this bow,
(b) the *maximum* velocity of this arrow (ignore the effect of gravity). ∎

Q 3.17 Self-assessment question

Look again at the events described in question 3.4. Suggest brief explanations, this time using the equation:

change in kinetic energy = work done by force
of a body   acting on body ∎

It is possible to explain observations in more than one way, and thinking about the energy changes involved is often a very useful way of explaining things. Energy methods are particularly useful because they involve considering *scalar* quantities.

E Experiment FM 3
Energy and momentum changes

The conservation of energy is investigated when elastic strain energy is transformed to kinetic energy of a moving trolley.

Safety design in cars

In a collision, the rapid stopping of the vehicle and its passengers mean that large forces are acting which can produce serious or fatal injury. In considering how to reduce these, energy and momentum considerations can be helpful.

$F \times$ stopping distance = change in kinetic energy
$F \times$ stopping time = change in momentum

Increasing the stopping time and stopping distance will reduce the forces acting during the collision. To achieve this, cars must be designed with front and rear structures which easily collapse on impact. The passengers are carried in a strong central compartment which slows down more gradually as the front or rear buckles. The passengers must be held by strong safety belts. The trouble is, as you may have noticed, that modern cars tend to collapse badly, even in minor collisions when travelling at low speed (10 miles per hour), and a way needs to be found of enabling cars to absorb the energy of minor shocks and recover their original shape. One solution is to build strong shock absorbing bumpers (figure 3.10). When the bumper hits something, the piston moves to the left. Fluid is forced through small holes in the dashpot and energy is absorbed gradually as a result.

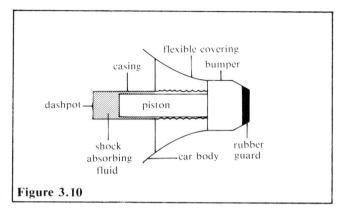

Figure 3.10

3.4 Energy changes during collisions

Q 3.18 Development question*

A trolley of mass 1.0 kg and velocity 0.5 m s⁻¹ collides with another stationary trolley of the same mass. A piece of plasticine at the point of impact ensures that the trolleys stick together after impact.

(a) What is the common velocity after impact?
(b) Show that the kinetic energy before impact is 0.125 J and after impact is 0.0625 J.
(c) Explain why the kinetic energy is not conserved.
(d) What, besides the two trolleys, must be included in the system if the total energy is to be conserved? ■

Q 3.19 Development question*

Figure 3.11 is a dramatic picture of the effect of the forces acting during a collision.

(a) What forms of energy are indicated by the photograph?
(b) What is likely to happen to the kinetic energy of the ball immediately after the instant recorded by this photograph? ■

During collisions some, or all, of the kinetic energy of the interacting bodies can be changed into potential energy which is stored temporarily in the force field between the atoms of the compressed matter (figure 3.12). The compressing forces become maximum as the masses stop moving towards each other and these interatomic forces then push the bodies apart.

Figure 3.11

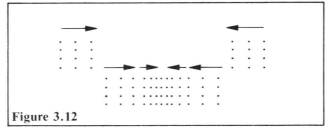

Figure 3.12

Q 3.20 Study question

(a) Find out the precise meaning of the terms 'perfectly elastic' and 'inelastic' when used to describe collisions.
(b) For a perfectly elastic collision, how does the work done in compressing each object compare with the energy released when they become uncompressed?
(c) What does this tell you about the way the force depends on the compression?
(d) Contrast this with the case of the inelastic collision. ■

Perfectly elastic collisions are found on the atomic scale, e.g. between gas molecules, between molecules of a gas and its container, and between nuclei of gas molecules and particles emitted by radioactive substances.

Super-elastic or hyper-elastic collisions can occur in which kinetic energy is actually increased during the collision, e.g. two vibrating molecules collide and, as a result, their total kinetic energy of translation is increased at the expense of their vibrational energy.

Q 3.21 Study question

What do you think is meant by an 'explosive collision'?
How might this be observed using trolleys? ■

Q 3.22 Self-assessment question

Why is it correct to say that steel is more elastic (or less inelastic) than rubber? What can you say about the very bouncy superballs? ■

E Experiment FM 4
The speed of a rifle bullet

This experiment uses the principle of conservation of momentum to find the speed of a bullet. The collision is inelastic, and the loss in kinetic energy can be estimated.

Solving problems on collisions

1 Select the closed system within which the conservation law can be applied.

2 Draw 'before' and 'after' diagrams, marking the masses and velocities involved.

3 Remember that the total vector momentum is constant in any direction in which no external forces act. So choose a line along which the law applies and mark one direction as positive.

4 Equate the total momentum before interaction to the total momentum after.

5 If the problem involves two-dimensional motion (see section 3.5), repeat (c) and (d) for a second direction, usually chosen at right angles to the first. If you need another equation, look for some way in which you can relate kinetic energies or relative velocities 'before' and 'after'. For example, for perfectly elastic collisions equate total kinetic energy before and after collision.

Q 3.23 Self-assessment question

A vehicle on a frictionless air track has a mass of 0.2 kg and it is moving at 5.0 m s^{-1} when it collides perfectly elastically with a stationary vehicle of mass 0.5 kg.

(a) Calculate the velocities of the vehicles after the interaction.

(b) Calculate the fraction of the original energy that is transferred to the second vehicle. ■

E Experiment FM5
A multiple collision — Newton's cradle

The aim of this experiment is to consider the momentum and energy changes in a multiple collision.

EXTENSION

Energy exchanges in elastic collisions.

In a perfectly elastic collision,

$$\frac{\text{relative velocity}}{\text{before collision}} = -\frac{\text{relative velocity}}{\text{after collision}}$$

$$(u_1 - u_2) = -(v_1 - v_2)$$

Q 3.24 Development question

Consider a mass m_1 with velocity u_1 colliding elastically with a mass m_2 with velocity u_2. Let the final velocities be v_1 and v_2.

(a) Write the equation representing the conservation of momentum.

(b) Write the equation representing the conservation of energy.

(c) From each of these equations find an expression for m_1/m_2, and equate these expressions.

(d) Simplify the result, remembering that

$$x^2 - y^2 = (x+y)(x-y) \blacksquare$$

Q 3.25 Self-assessment question

A moving body makes an elastic collision with a stationary body of the same mass. Use the principle of conservation of momentum and the relative velocity relationship to show that in this case momentum and energy are completely exchanged between the two bodies. ■

What happens in elastic collisions between a moving mass and a stationary one in cases where the masses are very different? Figure 3.13 shows the results of applying the two conservation laws to interactions between a very large and a very small mass.

A ball colliding elastically with the earth keeps virtually all its kinetic energy. This is also the case for perfectly elastic collisions between electrons and large gas atoms. If a very large mass hits a stationary small mass, the greatest velocity the small mass can acquire is twice that of the large mass. (The speed of a football can never quite reach twice the speed of your kicking foot.)

In these two extreme instances the energy transfer during the collision is negligible. It is when the colliding masses are equal that there is maximum energy transfer. This is true for colliding masses and also for interacting electric circuits. The maximum energy transfer from an amplifier to a loudspeaker takes place when the impedances of the two components (the 'inertias') are equal.

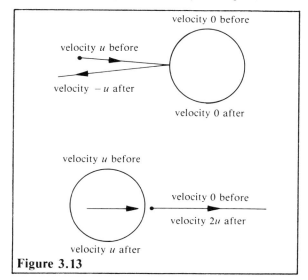

Figure 3.13

Figure 3.14 is a picture of a 'Newton's cradle' in which energy is exchanged by elastic collision between steel balls. If one ball swings down and collides with the rest its total kinetic energy will be transferred to the ball at the far end.

Q 3.26 Study question
Show, by applying the conservation laws to a Newton's cradle, that if two balls swing in at one end it is impossible for their combined energies to be given to one ball at the other end. ∎

Figure 3.14

3.5 Collisions in two dimensions

Collisions often occur in which the 'third-law pair' of forces is not acting in line with the direction of the original motion (figure 3.15).

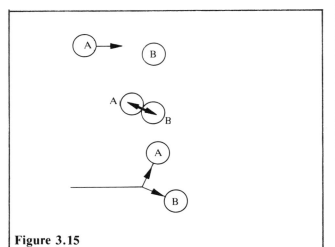
Figure 3.15

We do not need to know the direction in which the 'third-law pair' acts, since in any direction there will be equal and opposite components acting and so momentum will be conserved in that direction. So these collisions can be analysed by resolving the velocities into components along any two directions (normally perpendicular to each other) and using separate momentum equations for each direction.

Such an oblique collision is shown occurring on an atomic scale in figure 3.16. Figure 3.17 shows a similar event in which the collision between a moving and a stationary puck of equal mass has been recorded by multiflash photography.

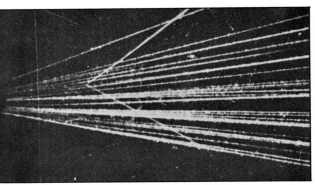
Figure 3.16

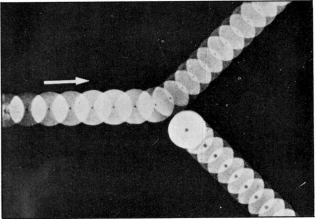
Figure 3.17

Q 3.27 Study question
Is momentum conserved in the collision of the pucks? (Use the successive images to compare velocities and remember that momentum and velocity are vector quantities which can be resolved.)∎

Q **3.28 Self-assessment question**

Assuming that the cloud chamber photograph in figure 3.16 records a perfectly elastic collision, what can you say about the masses of the colliding particles? (The plane of the collision tracks is not quite in the plane of the photograph, but calculations from this photograph and others taken at the same time from different angles show that the actual angle 'in space' between the tracks after collision is 90°.) ∎

EXTENSION

Q **3.29 Study question**

Show that in an elastic collision between particles of equal mass, one of which is initially at rest, the recoiling particles always move so that the angle between the directions of their velocities is 90°. ∎

AV **FM 1 Filmloop**
Collisions in two dimensions

A filmed record of a collision between frictionless pucks, from which calculations of velocities can be made.

3.6 Force as rate of change of momentum

Newton's second law can be stated (with quantities in the appropriate units) as:

resultant force = rate of change of momentum,

or

$$F = \frac{\Delta p}{\Delta t}$$

where Δp is the change in momentum and Δt is the time over which the momentum change occurs.

For bodies of constant mass this becomes

$$F = m\frac{\Delta v}{\Delta t} = ma$$

This is the equation which has been used to solve problems in chapter 2.

We can extend the analysis to situations where there are changes of mass, but velocities are constant. For these we can write:

$$F = v\frac{\Delta m}{\Delta t}$$

For example, consider a conveyor belt travelling with a steady horizontal velocity v. It is loaded with ore at the rate $\Delta m/\Delta t$. The belt exerts a force on this ore of $v(\Delta m/\Delta t)$. (Force = momentum gained per second by the ore.)

Q **3.30 Self-assessment question**

Ore is deposited at a uniform rate of 25 kg s⁻¹, with negligible kinetic energy, on to a conveyor belt moving horizontally with a speed of 4 m s⁻¹. Calculate
(a) the force required to maintain a constant velocity,
(b) the power required,
(c) the rate of increase of kinetic energy of the ore as it is moved by the conveyor belt.
(d) Why are the answers to parts (b) and (c) not the same? ∎

Q **3.31 Self-assessment question**

A horizontal jet of water carries 5×10^2 kg s⁻¹ at a velocity of 4 m s⁻¹. If this strikes the side of a ship and drops on to the sea with no horizontal velocity, what is the force acting on the ship? ∎

3.7 Powered flight

Consider the origin of the forces which lift giant rockets, accelerate aircraft to high speed and high altitude, and enable helicopters to 'defy gravity' as they hover.

Aerodynamic upthrust

An aeroplane achieves lift by the use of aerofoil-section wings. To understand how this is achieved, we start by considering Bernoulli's principle, which predicts that the pressure in a moving fluid decreases as the flow velocity increases.

Consider a small cube of fluid, which we shall assume is incompressible, flowing from a wide tube into a narrow tube, as shown in figure 3.18. The same volume per second must be flowing through each tube, so that the velocity must increase as the cross section decreases $(v_2 > v_1)$. A resultant force must act on the cube in this region (Newton's second law). This resultant force must be produced by the greater fluid pressure in the wider tube $(P_1 > P_2)$.

If the airflow past an aerofoil is streamlined as shown in figure 3.19, the air flowing along the upper surface will travel further and faster than the air flowing along the lower surface. Even though the air is compressible, and viscous forces also act, the pressure difference predicted by Bernoulli's principle still exists and provides an upthrust.

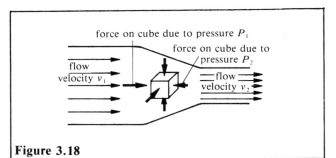

Figure 3.18

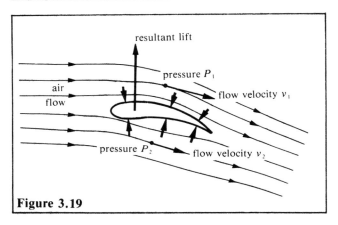

Figure 3.19

Q 3.32 Study question

Figure 3.20 shows the forces on an aeroplane travelling horizontally with constant velocity.
(a) Explain how thrust and drag forces are produced, and indicate briefly the factors which control the magnitude of these forces.
(b) Apply Newton's third law to identify and describe the forces acting on other bodies due to the moving aeroplane. ∎

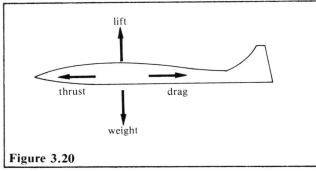

Figure 3.20

Bernoulli's equation for the pressure difference between two points at the same horizontal level in a non-viscous incompressible fluid is $P_2 - P_1 = \frac{1}{2}\rho(v_1{}^2 - v_2{}^2)$ where ρ is the density of the fluid and v_1 and v_2 the velocities at the two points.

Q 3.33 Self-assessment question

Assuming Bernoulli's equation is approximately true for the pressure difference across an aerofoil in moving air, as in figure 3.19, explain:
(a) how the shape of the aerofoil and the angle it makes with the airstream affect the lift force,
(b) why the lift on the aeroplane increases with its speed. ∎

Helicopters

Aeroplanes have to move through the air at high speed to remain airborne, since the aerodynamic upthrust depends on providing a high speed airflow past the aerofoil wings. A rotating aerofoil can provide a force which depends on the speed of rotation, not on the linear speed with which it moves through the air (figure 3.21).

Q **3.34 Self-assessment question**
(a) A student describes a helicopter as 'an aircraft with rotating wings'. His friend rejects this description, and says a helicopter is a plane with the propeller on top instead of at the front, so that air can be forced down by a rotating airscrew. Comment on these statements and say how you would obtain evidence to decide which description was right.
(b) How does a helicopter obtain forward propulsion?
(c) What purpose is served by the small propeller at the end of the fuselage? ∎

Figure 3.21

Rockets

In a rocket motor, the rapid combustion of fuel produces gaseous expansion. A forward thrust is exerted on the rocket and a high speed jet of gas emerges backwards. The momentum which the rocket acquires is equal to the momentum of the exhaust gases flowing out of the rocket (principle of conservation of momentum).

Force of gas on rocket = forward thrust
    = force of rocket on
      expelled gas
    = change in momentum
      per second.

$$\text{Thrust of rocket motor} = \frac{\text{mass ejected}}{\text{per second}} \times \frac{\text{velocity of jet}}{\text{relative to rocket}}$$

The analysis of the flight of a rocket is made more complex by the change in mass of the rocket, due to the high rate of fuel ejection which can be more than 10 000 kg s^{-1}, and the jettisoning of the stages (see figure 3.22). In a jet engine, by comparison, a typical rate of fuel ejection is 1 kg s^{-1}, so that the change in the jet aeroplane's mass can be neglected.

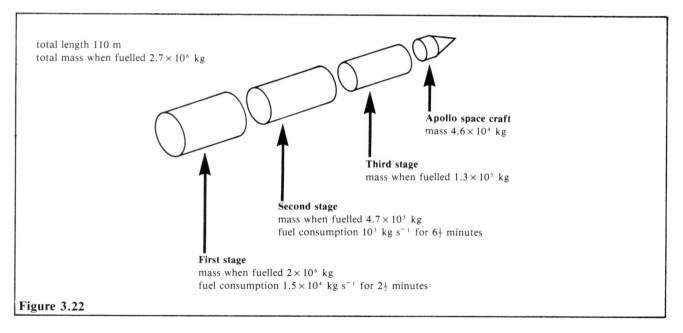

total length 110 m
total mass when fuelled 2.7×10^6 kg

Apollo space craft
mass 4.6×10^4 kg

Third stage
mass when fuelled 1.3×10^5 kg

Second stage
mass when fuelled 4.7×10^5 kg
fuel consumption 10^3 kg s^{-1} for $6\frac{1}{2}$ minutes

First stage
mass when fuelled 2×10^6 kg
fuel consumption 1.5×10^4 kg s^{-1} for $2\frac{1}{2}$ minutes

Figure 3.22

Q **3.35 Self-assessment question**
In some versions of the Saturn V rocket used in the American space exploration programme, the original total mass was 2.5×10^6 kg and the fuel was consumed at the rate of 1.25×10^4 kg s^{-1}. If the exhaust gas velocity relative to the rocket is taken as 4000 m s^{-1}, calculate the initial acceleration (at take-off). Why will this acceleration increase as the rocket rises vertically, if the rate of fuel consumption is constant (two reasons)? ■

Q **3.36 Self-assessment question**
Discuss the popular belief that in order to propel a rocket or jet-plane the exhaust gases must push against the air in the atmosphere. ■

EXTENSION

Rocket and jet propulsion

Q **3.37 Study question**
Describe briefly, with the help of diagrams, the main differences (in principle and construction) between rocket and jet propulsion. In your answer, comment on comparative values of fuel consumption and 'pay load'. ■

Q **3.38 Self-assessment question**
In a test of a jet engine, it is necessary to simulate the conditions of a plane flying at 100 m s^{-1}. The engine is mounted on a test bed and air is taken in at 20 kg s^{-1} and a velocity of 100 m s^{-1}. After compression and combustion, the exhaust gases are ejected at 500 m s^{-1}. What must be the rate of consumption of fuel if the engine develops a thrust of 9.0×10^3 N? (Remember that the burnt fuel is part of the exhaust gas.) ■

3.8 Frames of reference

In your experiments on Newton's laws and the conservation of momentum, you viewed motion from a fixed point on the earth – your frame of reference. However, the observed motion of bodies depends on the movement of the observer as well as that of the bodies observed. So we must see whether the laws of mechanics and the conservation principles apply for observers in other frames of reference.

Q **3.39 Development question**
What would appear to happen to the speeds of colliding bodies, as measured by a multiflash photograph, if the camera was moving past the track at 0.2 m s^{-1} to the left? ■

All the observed velocities would change by 0.2 m s^{-1} to the right. This would certainly change the picture, but if you added up the momenta before and after collision you would find that the principle of momentum conservation still applied. You would also find that the observed loss of kinetic energy was the same whether the camera was moving or fixed.

A frame of reference in which the conservation laws apply is called an *inertial frame of reference*. We have just noted that a frame of reference travelling at constant velocity relative to an inertial frame is itself an inertial frame. In all inertial frames Newton's laws still apply. If a frictionless puck is placed at rest on a table, it will seem to remain at rest when viewed by a stationary observer, even if the table moves underneath it. If the puck and table remain stationary and the observer moves at constant velocity then the puck will seem to move at constant velocity. In both cases the observer is in an inertial frame. In both cases a resultant force of zero produces no change in observed velocity, i.e. the velocity has a constant value, which can be zero (Newton's 1st law).

If you are in an aeroplane there is no way of knowing whether it is flying with uniform velocity at 6000 m or is stationary on the ground, except by looking out of the window.

However, if the observer is in an accelerated frame of reference Newton's laws no longer operate. A stone acted on by gravitational force accelerates to the ground according to an observer in an inertial frame, but if the observer is falling with the stone he observes a stone acted on by gravitational force but remaining at rest relative to him. A rotating frame of reference is another example of a non-inertial frame of reference.

Q 3.40 Self-assessment question

A lorry carrying a block of ice on its otherwise empty flat surface, pulls up sharply at some traffic signals. What does the driver's mate see, looking from the cab, and what does an observer see looking down from a sixth-floor balcony? For which observer do Newton's laws seem to operate? Explain. ∎

Summary

In this chapter you have seen how the two key principles of conservation of momentum and conservation of energy can be applied to systems of interacting bodies. The conservation of momentum applies not just at the beginning and end but at every moment in the interaction. The same is true for *total* energy conservation, though we have seen how kinetic energy can be converted into internal energy of the colliding bodies and so kinetic energy may not be conserved.

In chapter 2 we stated that Newton's law must be modified by quantum considerations when dealing with very small particles (molecular, atomic and nuclear), but both momentum and energy appear to be conserved in these circumstances. Experimentally, the conservation laws have proved invaluable in analysing atomic and nuclear interactions and measuring the mass and energy of sub-atomic particles. In 1930 a hypothetical particle, the neutrino, was proposed in an attempt to solve a disagreement between the observed beta emission from radioactive materials and the conservation laws. Neutrinos and antineutrinos were only detected experimentally much later, in 1956.

Comprehension exercise

Analysis of an accident simulation

In their investigations into passenger safety, the Transport and Road Research Laboratory simulate accidents by using remotely controlled test cars which they direct at rigid concrete barriers. Drivers and passengers are simulated by the use of carefully designed models. Cars and models are fitted with instruments which enable the observers to measure velocities, accelerations and strains. Strategically placed cameras enable position changes to be recorded throughout the impact (figure 3.23). The results then have to be translated into the practical situations which are encountered on the road, with cars controlled and occupied by human beings.

Figure 3.23

Before considering methods of reducing the risk of injury, we need to examine the main changes which occur in the collision. After hitting the wall, the car moves through a small distance before coming to rest. During this motion the front of the car crumples. Meanwhile, the driver continues to move forward until his body strikes the object immediately in front of him.

It is this latter impact which causes injury. *The extent of the injury might be expected to depend on:*
the speed of impact,
the mass of the driver,
the resistance exerted by the object struck.

A car travelling at about 10 m s^{-1} crashes into a rigid wall. Between the time (reckoned as $t = 0$) at which the car first makes contact with the wall (figure 3.24a) and the time at which it comes to rest (figure 3.24b) the engine compartment at the front is crushed so that its length is shortened by 0.5 m, whilst the main body of the car, including the padding and dashboard, is decelerating. The graph in figure 3.24d shows how this deceleration of the main body of the car varies with time.

Questions

1 Explain, in terms of the laws of motion, the sentence in italics.

2 A scientist says 'the area under the graph is roughly 100×0.1 which gives about 10 m s^{-1} so that's consistent'. Explain his statement.

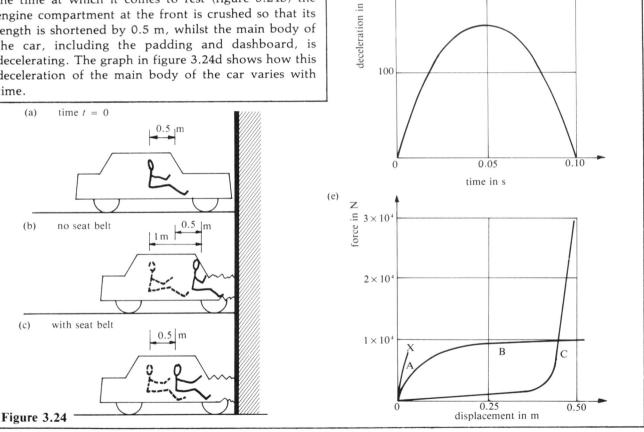

Figure 3.24

3 Sketch a graph of the velocity of the main body of the car against time over the time interval shown in figure 3.24d. Label the axes and explain how your sketch is related to figure 3.24d.

4 Consider a passenger in the car who is *not* wearing a safety belt. The dashboard padding is 0.5 m away from him before the crash (figure 3.24a) so that he moves a total distance of 1 m, relative to the ground, between time $t = 0$ and the moment that he hits the dashboard (figure 3.24b). Assuming that he moves forward freely during this interval and that he is then stopped by the padding which deforms a total of 15 cm, draw a sketch graph, using the same axes as for question 3, of his velocity relative to the ground as a function of time. What is his velocity relative to the padding when he hits it?

5 Consider a passenger who *is* wearing a safety belt. Assume first that it holds him *very firmly* to the car seat throughout the crash (figure 3.24c). If his mass is 70 kg, estimate the maximum force exerted on him during the crash and explain at what time during the crash this maximum force is exerted.

6 The curves A, B, C (figure 3.24e) are curves of force exerted on the passenger by a seat belt against the forward displacement of the passenger relative to the seat as the seat belt 'gives'. Curve A is for a belt which breaks at the point X: discuss whether this belt will give complete protection, some protection, or no protection at all.

7 Curves B and C are for seat belts of different design and made of different materials. Compare B and C in terms of the forces experienced by passengers when a car decelerates as in figure 3.24d. Explain the advantages of the belt which you think is the more suitable.

Questions on objectives

1 Give one form of the statement of the principle of the conservation of momentum. Explain the term 'isolated closed system'.

(objectives 1 and 3)

2 Define the impulse of a force.
The graph in figure 3.25 shows how the force exerted by a truck of mass 2.0 kg on another of mass 1.0 kg varied with time during an elastic collision. Estimate the approximate change of momentum experienced by the 1.0 kg truck and also what its change of velocity would have been. Sketch the graph and on the same sketch show how the force exerted by the 1.0 kg truck on the 2.0 kg truck varied with time.

(objectives 2 and 4)

3 When a golfer hits a long drive, his club is in contact with the ball for about 1/2000 s. The ball leaves the club at a speed of about 75 m s⁻¹.
(a) If the mass of the ball is 50 g, what is the mean accelerating force?
(b) How does this force compare with the force that the golfer would exert on the ball if he stood on it? (Take $g = 10$ N kg⁻¹, mass of golfer = 75 kg.).

(objectives 2 and 4)

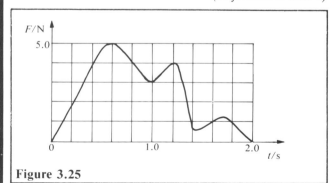

Figure 3.25

4 A bricklayer breaks a brick by holding it in his hand and striking it with the hammer. Yet the same hammer blow applied directly to his hand would produce considerable pain. Explain the difference.

(objectives 1 and 4)

5 A passenger in a car travelling at 20 m s⁻¹ has a mass of 80 kg. The car suffers a head-on collision and stops. The seat belt holding the passenger brings him to rest in 0.20 s. Assuming the seat belt exerts a constant force on the passenger while he is brought to rest, calculate the value of this force.

(objectives 2 and 4)

6 A railway truck of mass 4×10^4 kg, moving at a velocity of 3 m s⁻¹, collides with another truck of mass 2×10^4 kg which is at rest. The couplings join and the trucks move off together. What fraction of the first truck's initial kinetic energy remains as kinetic energy of the two trucks after the collision? Is energy conserved in a collision such as this? Explain your answer briefly.

(objective 4)

7 In radioactive decay, a radon nucleus of mass 3.5×10^{-25} kg emits an alpha particle of mass 6.4×10^{-27} kg with an energy of 1.0×10^{-12} J. Calculate
(a) the speed of the alpha particle,
(b) the speed of recoil of the remains of the parent nucleus.

(objective 4)

8 A motor car is running with a constant velocity along a horizontal road. Draw a sketch of one wheel on the road showing the direction the car is moving in and the direction and point of action of the frictional force from the road on the wheel. Indicate on the diagram the force which propels the car forward. Explain how Newton's third law can be applied to the forces acting on the tyre.

(objective 4)

Chapter

4

Aim

In this chapter you will observe and analyse the motion of bodies moving in circular paths. The forces acting on these bodies will be calculated using Newton's laws. The ideas developed will be used to explain various applications, from orbiting planets to spin driers.

Objectives

When you have completed the work in this chapter you should be able to:

1 Use the following scientific terms correctly: angular velocity, linear speed, uniform circular motion, centripetal force, centripetal acceleration.

2 Recall and apply the equations

$$a = \frac{v^2}{r} \quad \text{and} \quad F = \frac{mv^2}{r}$$

3 Calculate the forces needed to keep an object moving in horizontal and vertical circles.

4 Identify the different effects experienced by an observer viewing a rotating system from the outside and from the inside.

5 Describe how 'gravity effects' may be artificially induced in a space station, and perform calculations to determine the magnitude of 'artificial gravity'.

6 Analyse the motion of bodies moving in a circular path by applying the ideas of centripetal acceleration and force.

Experiments in chapter 4

FM6 Motion in a circular orbit
(1 hour)

References

Akrill	Chapter 4
Duncan MM	Chapter 7
Nelkon	Chapter 2
Thorning	Chapter 6
Whelan	Chapters 2 and 3
Williams	Chapter 14

Chapter 4

Study time: $1\frac{1}{2}$ weeks

4.1 Introduction

There are many examples in the universe of bodies travelling in curved paths: planets moving in elliptical (nearly circular) orbits, racing cars cornering at speed, clothes in a spin drier and orbiting electrons. We shall be looking at the ideas developed to explain motion in a straight line, and see how they can help us describe circular motion.

If a body is moving in a curved path, its velocity must be changing (even if its speed is constant) because velocity is a vector quantity which can change in magnitude, or in direction, or both. By observing bodies moving in a curved path we shall try to discover what force produces their change in velocity.

We have already looked at motion in a straight line in which bodies either move in the same direction as the force (and so speed up) or move in exactly the opposite direction (and so slow down). But what happens when a body is moving in one direction and a force acts on it in another direction? Figure 4.1 represents the path of a body which is acted on by a force at right angles to the original motion of the body. Figure 4.2 shows the same situation – a constant force of gravity acting vertically on a mass projected horizontally.

Q **4.1 Self-assessment question**
In figure 4.2,
(a) what is the direction of the acceleration,
(b) what changes in velocity are shown (change in speed, direction, or both)? ∎

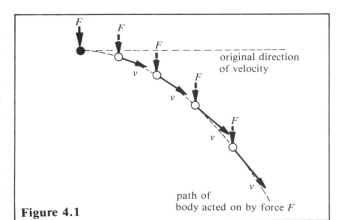

Figure 4.1

original direction of velocity

path of body acted on by force F

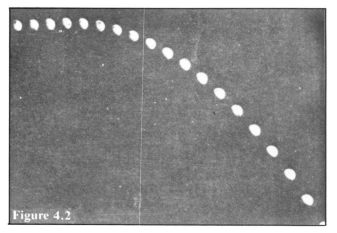

Figure 4.2

A constant force always acting in the same direction makes a body move along a parabola.

Now consider a simpler case of a body moving with *constant speed* in a circle. We can produce this kind of motion by whirling a rubber bung round on the end of a string (figure 4.3).

Q **4.2 Development question**
(a) If the bung in figure 4.3 has a steady speed, is there any acceleration or component of acceleration along the direction of motion?
(b) Is the velocity of the bung changing at a steady rate as it goes round the circle?
(c) What force enables the bung to move in a circle? Is it a force of constant size? Which way does the force act? ∎

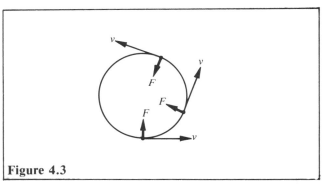

Figure 4.3

For uniform circular motion (motion at constant speed in a circle) there can be no component acceleration along the direction of motion, so the acceleration must always be at right angles to the motion and directed along a radius towards the centre. Since the body is turning steadily at constant speed, the acceleration must be constant in magnitude (but always changing in direction) and a constant force towards the centre is required to produce this motion. This is provided by the tension in the string.

Q 4.3 Study question
Why is the term 'centripetal force' used to describe the force shown in figure 4.3? ■

The multiflash photograph (figure 4.4) shows a frictionless puck held by a string and travelling at constant speed round a circle. The bright flash in the centre is produced by the burning of the string at that moment.

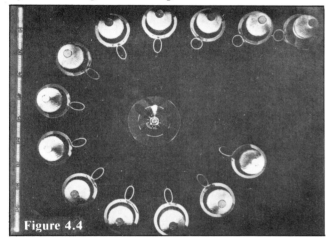
Figure 4.4

Q 4.4 Self-assessment question
Describe the motion of the puck in figure 4.4 after the string burns, and say which law applies to this motion. ■

Q 4.5 Self-assessment question
For each of the following cases of bodies moving in a circle, state what force or forces act *on* the body towards the centre of the circle:
(a) a car going round a bend,
(b) a train on a curved track,
(c) clothes in a spin drier,
(d) the moon orbiting the earth. ■

4.2 Calculating the centripetal acceleration

If a body moves in a circle its motion can be described by its angular velocity or by its linear speed. You may need to refer to the Student's Handbook, Section 10.4, in preparation for the next question.

Q 4.6 Study question
(a) Use the definition of an angle measured in radians to obtain an expression for the length of arc AB in figure 4.5 and hence show that for small angles $\sin \delta\theta \approx \delta\theta$.
(b) What is the relationship between angular velocity ω and linear speed v? ■

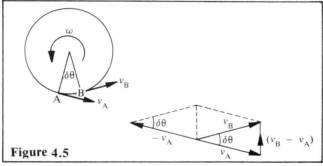
Figure 4.5

Q 4.7 Development question*
A body is moving round a circle radius r with constant angular velocity ω (figure 4.5). It moves from point A to point B in a brief time of δt. Its velocity changes from v_A to v_B in this time (change in direction but not magnitude).
(a) What distance round the circle does the body move in a time δt?
(b) Calculate the speed v in terms of the distance travelled in the time δt.

(c) Use the vector diagram in figure 4.5 to show that the change in velocity in time δt is $v\,\delta\theta$ if $\delta\theta$ is small.
(d) What is the average acceleration of the body between A and B (rate of change of velocity)?
(e) Hence show that the acceleration of the body at any point is v^2/r towards the centre. Show that this centripetal acceleration can also be expressed as $r\omega^2$.
(f) If the body has mass m, what centripetal force must act to produce the uniform circular motion (give two equivalent expressions)? ■

Q 4.8 Self-assessment question
A frictionless puck of mass 300 g moves in a horizontal circle round a fixed point to which it is attached by a string of length 0.50 m. If it makes one revolution in 2.0 seconds what is the tension in the string?
(You can assume $\pi^2 = 10$.) ■

When a conker is whirled in a horizontal circle, the string itself will not be horizontal. The point at which the string is held will be above the plane of the circle.

Q 4.9 Self-assessment question
(a) What force, in addition to the centripetal force, does the string provide?
(b) Draw a diagram showing the forces on the conker.
(c) Write out the equation expressing the fact that the conker does not fall.
(d) Write out the equation expressing the fact that the conker is being accelerated towards the centre of the circle.
(e) What happens to the angle which the string makes with the vertical if the angular velocity of the conker increases? ■

Q 4.10 Self-assessment question
Figure 4.6 shows a skater spinning. Why does her skirt seem to fly outwards, when the force acting is directed inwards towards the centre? ■

Figure 4.6

EXTENSION

Q 4.11 Self assessment question
A mass is moving with constant angular velocity ω in a horizontal circle at the end of a string length l inclined to the vertical at an angle θ. Show that the tension in the string is $m\omega^2 l$ and that $\cos\theta = g/\omega^2 l$. ■

E Experiment FM 6
Motion in a circular orbit
In this experiment you will obtain evidence to verify that the centripetal force is mv^2/r.

AV FM 7 Film loop
Dynamics of circular motion
This film loop shows you how to analyse the motion of a puck in a circle and so calculate the force needed to keep a model aircraft moving in a circle.

4.3 Going around the bend
A car going round a corner at a steady speed is accelerated, and a centripetal force must be acting. Consider the ways in which these forces are provided to enable cars, trains, aircraft and bicycles to turn.

Q 4.12 Self-assessment question
(a) A car of mass 750 kg is taking a corner with a flat horizontal surface and a radius of 10 m. If the sideways friction forces cannot exceed 1/10 of the weight of the vehicle, what is the maximum speed at which it can take the bend? (Assume $g = 10\ \text{N kg}^{-1}$.)
(b) Which piece of the above information is not needed? Explain your answer. ■

The frictional push of the road on the tyres is not the only force acting on the car. Air resistance also acts, and the resultant of these forces must provide the 'sideways' or centripetal force.

Q 4.13 Study question
Sketch the *horizontal* forces acting on a car rounding a bend, showing their direction and the resultant centripetal force. ■

Because friction is a limited force, a car travelling too fast may not get round the bend even though the wheels are pointing in the right direction. It may skid or turn over. We shall consider why bodies topple over in the next chapter. One way of reducing the possibility of slipping at a corner is to slope or bank the road so that the normal contact push of the road acting on the car produces a central force. For a particular speed, this force will produce exactly the centripetal force required. At other speeds some frictional force will be called into play.

Q 4.14 Study question
Show that, for a vehicle taking a bend at speed v, the banking of the curve to eliminate side slip (any tendency to skid) is given by

$$\tan \theta = \frac{v^2}{gr}$$

where θ is the angle between the road surface and the horizontal. ∎

Q 4.15 Self-assessment question
(a) British Rail's new high-speed trains are designed to travel at 200 km h⁻¹. Calculate the banking needed on a track of radius 0.25 km if that speed is to be sustained without the train trying to push the rails out of place (hint: this means that the force on the train produced by the rails will be perpendicular to the ground).
(b) What will passengers feel if the train takes this banked curve at speeds below 200 km h⁻¹?
(c) What will passengers feel if the train takes the curve at speeds above 200 km h⁻¹? ∎

An aircraft can only turn if it banks so that the lift force produced by its wings is no longer acting vertically. A component of this lift force then provides the centripetal force. The tailplane also plays an important role, and in a delta-wing aircraft like Concorde this is the most important factor. Raising the wing flaps produces an increased pressure above the wing and lowering the wing flaps reduces the pressure (figure 4.7). The result is a lateral force on the tail fin and a rotation of the plane to starboard (dotted arrow).

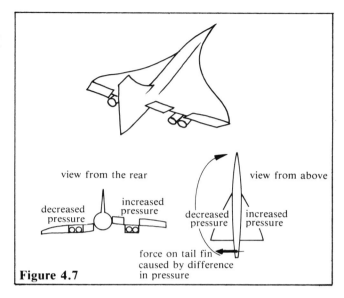

view from the rear

view from above

decreased pressure

increased pressure

decreased pressure

increased pressure

force on tail fin caused by difference in pressure

Figure 4.7

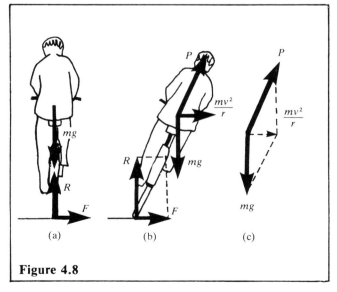

(a)　　　　(b)　　　　(c)

Figure 4.8

A cyclist would not get round a corner without slipping if he remained vertical (figure 4.8a). If he tried to do this, the resultant force F would act along the ground, so that the bottom of the wheels would manage to move round the corner but the poor cyclist would continue to travel in a straight line.

Figure 4.8b shows how a cyclist negotiates a corner. R is the normal contact push of the ground on the cycle, and F is the tangential frictional push of the ground on the cycle. The resultant of forces R and F is a force P acting through the centre of gravity of the rider and the machine. In figure 4.8c the resultant of forces P and mg is a centripetal force acting through the centre of gravity. This ensures that both cycle and cyclist accelerate towards the centre of curvature of the bend, and get round the bend safely. In the next chapter we shall consider why the cyclist does not topple over if he negotiates a corner in this way.

4.4 Defying gravity

A bucket of water can be swung around without spilling and a pilot loops the loop confident that he will stay in his seat in the aircraft. Think about the forces acting on a body and its kinetic energy as it moves in a vertical circle.

Q **4.16 Development question***
Figure 4.9 shows a body of mass m moving in a vertical circle on the end of a string.

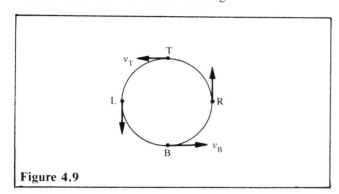

Figure 4.9

(a) What force provides the centripetal force at L, R and B?

(b) What two forces may provide the centripetal force at T?

(c) Why does the speed change as the mass moves from B to T?

(d) Calculate $v_B^2 - v_T^2$ for a circle of radius r.

(e) Derive expressions for the tension in the string when the mass is at the top and when it is at the bottom of the circle and show that the difference between these tensions is $6mg$.

(f) What is the value of the velocity at the top if the body moves in a circle but the tension in the string is zero? ■

Q **4.17 Self-assessment question**
Estimate the minimum angular velocity at which a bucket of water must pass over your head at arm's length in a vertical circle if you are to remain dry. ■

4.5 Spin driers and centrifuges

In a spin drier the clothes move around in a circle because the walls of the spinning cylinder provide the centripetal force. The holes in the cylinder are small enough to prevent clothes going through, but large and frequent enough not to impede the water. Very large forces are required to keep a mass spinning in a circle at high speed. The clothes fibres cannot exert these forces on the water, which therefore does not have the necessary acceleration to move in a circle.

Q **4.18 Self-assessment question**
(a) In which direction will the water travel when it is 'thrown out' of a spin drier?

(b) Calculate the maximum force a water molecule will need to keep it in the spinner, if the cylinder is turning 6000 times every minute and has a diameter of 0.5 m. Take the mass of a water molecule as 3×10^{-25} kg.

(c) An automatic washing-machine manufacturer advertises on TV that they have increased the rotational frequency of the cylinder from 5000 to 8000 revs per minute. What percentage increase in the 'squeezing force' does this represent? ■

You are familiar with the way cream rises in a milk bottle which is left standing. This is because the cream is less dense than the milk, and gravity produces a variation in liquid pressure throughout the milk (pressure increasing with depth).

What happens when a tube containing liquid is spun in a centrifuge? Figure 4.10 a shows a cross-section of such a tube. A small element of liquid of mass Δm in the spinning tube must have a centripetal force $\Delta m\, v^2/r$ acting on it. This is provided by the unequal forces set up by the pressure differences in the tube. If these are given by P_1 and P_2, with A the cross-section of the tube, then $(P_2-P_1)A = \Delta m\, v^2/r$. So pressure increases with distance from the axis. If a cylindrical particle (cross section A') of low density is in the tube shown in figure 4.10 b, $(P_2-P_1)A'$ may be greater than the force required to keep the particle moving in a circle radius r. As a result it will move along the tube towards the centre. For a particle of high density the force $(P_2 - P_1)A'$ may not be large enough to provide the centripetal force and it will move away from the axis of rotation.

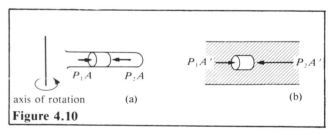

Figure 4.10

Centrifuges have proved indispensable in separating particles which are so nearly identical that no other method is effective; for example uranium 235 and uranium 238 have been separated by the centrifuging of UF_6 vapour containing molecules of both these isotopes. Even the two types of sperm cells have been separated by the centrifuge.

Q 4.19 Study question

(a) Explain why a centrifuge will separate solid suspensions from the liquid they are in, for example, red blood cells from blood plasma in medical investigations.
(b) What factor will be crucial in determining the time it takes to separate the suspension from the liquid? ■

Q 4.20 Self-assessment question

(a) Do the blades of a helicopter rotor stretch when rotating?
(b) Explain how the centripetal force is provided for a segment of the blade.
(c) Predict what might happen if the blade spins too fast. (Hint: find out where the largest forces are acting.)
(d) Explain how the centripetal force is provided for a tyre on a rotating car wheel by considering the forces acting on a small arc of the tyre.
(e) Predict and explain what might happen to the tyre at excessively high speeds. ■

Background reading

An interesting application of circular motion is the use of rotating moulds in casting metals. Details of these methods can be found in *The way things work*.

Artificial gravity

The centrifuge separates cream from milk in seconds rather than days by producing an enhanced gravity effect. In the same way, an artificial gravity effect could be produced in a space station by rotating it. By building a doughnut-shaped space station and spinning it, spacemen can live in an environment where there is an 'up' and 'down', and they can feel their weight acting on the 'floor'.

Q 4.21 Self-assessment question

A space station is to be put in orbit several thousand kilometres above the surface of the earth. It will be provided with 'artificial gravity', obtained by building the station in the form of a ring-shaped doughnut, and then making it spin about an axis through O, perpendicular to the plane of the ring (figure 4.11a). Figure 4.11b shows a semi-circular half of the space station, and also a square-shaped room ABCD in which people can live. E is the centre point of the room.
(a) Which is the floor (i.e. place to stand on) in room ABCD? What happens to an object released at E (as seen by a man in the room) when the station is steadily rotating? What happens to an object released at E when the rotation is still being speeded up to its final value?
(b) The length of the radius OE is 40 metres. The rate of rotation is just sufficient to provide, at E, an 'artificial gravity' having the same effect as that of the actual gravitational acceleration g at the earth's surface. What is the tangential speed of E in its motion round O (metres per second)?
(c) A man in a space suit is sent out, through an air lock, to tighten nuts on the outer rim of the station. The man is safely held by a rope, but he lets go of the spanner. Use Newton's first law to explain what happens to the spanner.

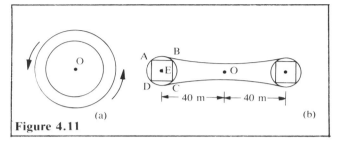

Figure 4.11

(d) How could the station be set rotating by the use of two jets? Where would you mount the jets? Could it be set rotating by one jet only, and if so, what advantage is there in using two?
(e) Discuss whether an electric motor could be used, instead of the jets, to set the station rotating. ■

Centripetal and centrifugal

All the effects of circular motion have been explained from the viewpoint of an observer outside the spinning system, in an inertial frame of reference. We know that from this viewpoint Newton's laws are valid, and bodies have been observed to have a centripetal acceleration because of centripetal force. In the absence of that central force they travel tangentially at constant velocity.

For an observer inside a rotating space station in an accelerated frame of reference things would seem very different. As far as he is concerned 'up' has become a direction towards the centre of rotation and he feels the effects of a force making bodies accelerate away from the centre – a 'centrifugal' force. His body and the spring balances he uses all convince him that this force is real, though viewing the system from the outside we have no need to invent such a force. The trouble with inventing forces is that we would have to do it for every different frame of reference. If our observations were all made on a rapidly accelerating bus we would have to invent a force tending to push all objects to the back of the bus; in fact we would have to rewrite mechanics for every different frame of reference. A much better idea is to stick to Newton's mechanics, look at the problem from outside the spinning system and forget about inventing new forces. So until you become an astronaut avoid centrifugal forces!

Remember also that when you draw a force diagram for a body moving in a circle you must end up with a resultant force towards the centre. Don't be tempted to add an extra fictitious force just to make the object look as though it is in equilibrium when, of course, it isn't.

Q **4.23 Study question**
Is it valid to use the term centrifugal force if you are inside the rotating space station? Is there any way you could tell whether this was a universal force (like gravity) or only the effect produced by observing within a rotating frame of reference? ■

Questions on objectives

1 For each of the statements in parts (a)–(d) choose one of the following terms (A–D) with which it is closely associated.

A circular path
B centripetal force
C centripetal acceleration
D tangentially

(a) The tension in the string holding a conker which is moving in a circle.
(b) The direction in which a conker will fly if the string breaks.
(c) The rate of change of velocity of a car taking a bend at a steady speed.
(d) The path of an object to which a force of constant magnitude is applied, this force being always at right angles to its direction of travel.

(objective 1)

2 Consider a car of mass 1200 kg taking a bend of radius 100 m at a speed of 72 km h^{-1}.
(a) Calculate the acceleration the car is undergoing.
(b) What is the resultant force towards the centre necessary to keep the car travelling round the bend? What is the source of this centripetal force?
(c) Calculate the angle at which the road should be banked to eliminate any tendency for the car to side slip.

(objectives 2, 3 and 6)

3 A man spins a bucket full of water in a vertical circle on the end of his arm. The effective radius of his arms and the bucket is 1 metre and g = 10 m s^{-2}.
(a) State when the tension in his arms is at a maximum and when it is at a minimum.
(b) Calculate the minimum angular velocity the bucket must have at the top of its swing if the water does not fall out.

(objectives 3 and 6)

4 A steel ball of mass 0.1 kg is released from the top of the track shown in figure 4.12.
(a) What is the reaction of the rail on the ball when it is at the top of the loop?

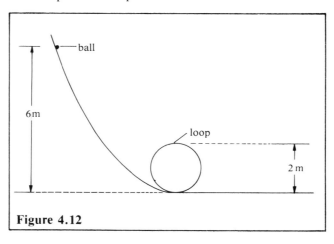

Figure 4.12

(b) What is the reaction force of the rail on the ball when the ball is half-way between the top and the bottom of the loop?
(c) What is the direction of the resultant force acting on the ball when it is in this position?
(d) Explain why it is possible for a ball to move in a circle with an acceleration which is not acting towards the centre of the circle.

(objectives 2, 3 and 6)

5 By using a 'spoked wheel' type of space station you can produce an artificial gravity for the occupants and allow space ships to dock easily. Discuss how this is so. You may find the following points worth considering in your answer.
How would you produce a 'gravity' of 1 g?
How big would the space station be for this?
Where would you dock a space ship? Why?

(objectives 4, 5)

Chapter 5

Aim

So far in this unit you have applied the laws of mechanics to objects which could be considered as point masses. In this chapter you will apply the same laws to study the effect of forces on rigid bodies. Concepts and laws will be developed to account for the observed behaviour of rotating discs, flywheels and vehicles.

Objectives

When you have completed the work in this chapter you should be able to:

1 Use the following scientific terms correctly: radius of gyration, centre of mass.

2 Define the following scientific terms: torque, moment, couple, moment of inertia.

3 Recall the recommended symbols and the units of the following: torque, angular momentum, moment of inertia, angular velocity, angular acceleration.

4 State the similarities and differences between the behaviour of rotating bodies and bodies travelling with linear velocities.

5 State the equilibrium conditions for a body acted on by coplanar forces.

6 Identify the factors which determine the moment of inertia of a body.

7 State and apply the law of conservation of angular momentum.

8 Perform calculations to determine the magnitude and direction of a torque and its effect on a body (i.e. application of the equation $T = I\alpha$).

9 Perform calculations to determine the work done on a body and the changes in its rotational kinetic energy.

Experiments in Chapter 5

FM 7   Effect of a torque
($\frac{3}{4}$ hour – two students required)
FM 8   Moment of inertia of a disc
(1 hour)
FM 9   Moment of inertia of a flywheel
($\frac{3}{4}$ hour)

References

Akrill	Chapters 11, 12 and 13
Duncan MM	Chapter 7
Nelkon	Chapter 3
Thorning	Chapters 6, 7 and 8
Whelan	Chapters 6 and 7
Williams	Chapters 10 and 19

Chapter

5

Study time: $1\frac{1}{2}$ weeks

5.1 Introduction

This chapter discusses the effect of forces on rigid bodies. A *rigid* body is one which stays roughly the same shape when acted on by a force. This means that if a force is applied at a particular point in a rigid body it affects the motion of all the particles of the body in a predictable way.

Think of a bicycle wheel set spinning when the bicycle is turned upside down. Although the wheel is not travelling anywhere it was necessary to provide a force along the rim to start it rotating. If you try to stop it with your hand you soon realise that it has energy because of its rotation and it needs a force applied at the rim to slow it down. Of course, there must have been other forces acting on the axle to hold the wheel in the frame. If the wheel had been outside the frame, then an impulse applied to the rim could have set it rolling along the ground. In this case the wheel would be rotating and at the same time the whole wheel would be travelling somewhere.

We say the wheel has *rotational* and *translational* motion. Pure translational motion means that every part of the body is moving in the same direction with the same speed at a particular instant; the motion is pure rotational motion if each particle of the body moves in a circle about some axis of rotation.

Q **5.1 Self-assessment question**
A trolley is attached to a hanging weight by a string which passes over a pulley. Say which moving parts of the system have:
(a) translational motion,
(b) rotational motion,
(c) both translational and rotational motion. ∎

So far in our study of forces and motion we have assumed that forces acted on point masses (particles) to produce translational acceleration. Now we shall discover that the point of action of a force determines whether the body has rotational acceleration, translational acceleration or both. As you study the rotational motion of bodies you will notice the very close parallel between the terms and equations in linear dynamics and the terms and equations dealing with rotational motion of bodies. Once you have mastered the laws of linear motion, rotational motion is easy!

5.2 Equilibrium

A particle is in *equilibrium* if its acceleration is zero. If the particle's velocity is also zero we say it is in *static* equilibrium. This use of the word 'equilibrium' is rather different from the everyday use. Note the precise definition above.

Q **5.2 Self-assessment question**
State the conditions necessary for the equilibrium of a particle (or point mass). Is it possible for a moving particle to be in equilibrium? ∎

Now consider a body which can have both translational and rotational motion. The *torque* or moment of a force is its turning effect about a particular axis. We use the word moment when we are relating the turning effect to the force causing it. We use torque for the general turning effect of one or many forces.

Q **5.3 Development question***
(a) What is the unit of torque?
(b) What are the dimensions of torque?
(c) Suggest what condition is fulfilled if a body is not rotating, even though it is acted on by several forces all in the same plane but with different lines of action.
(d) Would the same conditions be fulfilled if the body was rotating at a constant speed?
(e) What further conditions must be satisfied if the body has no translational acceleration? ∎

5.4 Development question *

Figure 5.1 shows how a top can be set spinning by hand.

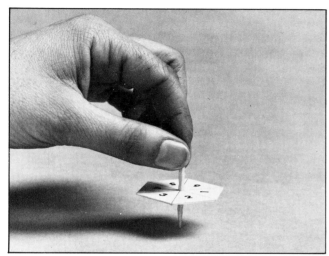

Figure 5.1

(a) Sketch the horizontal forces acting on the top.
(b) How do you know that the two horizontal forces acting are equal and opposite? ∎

A *couple* is a system of forces which produces only a turning effect (rotational acceleration). A couple may be a pair of forces, as in figure 5.1, or many forces like the 'couple' produced by a wound-up watch spring.

5.5 Study question

(a) Show that the torque produced by a couple is Fd when d is the perpendicular distance between the lines of action of the two equal parallel but opposite forces F.
(b) Show that the turning effect of a couple is the same for any axis perpendicular to the plane of the forces. ∎

Equilibrium for coplanar forces

If several forces act in the same plane on a body then we can say:
1 the resultant of all the forces is zero;
2 the resultant torque is zero. (The sum of clockwise moments about any point is equal to the sum of the anticlockwise moments about that point.)

If three forces act on a body their lines of action must all pass through the same point to satisfy these two conditions. If the third force does not pass through the intersection of the first two then there is a resultant torque about that point of intersection.

5.6 Self-assessment question

(a) Figure 5.2 shows a mountaineer in equilibrium under the action of three forces acting in the same plane. Sketch in the forces and estimate the tension in the rope if the mountaineer weighs 800 N.
(b) Why can three forces which do not act in the same plane never have a zero resultant? ∎

Centre of mass

When an athlete throws a discus he uses a single force to give the discus rotational and translation motion. Figure 5.5 shows a pair of coupled pucks set moving by a force so that the system rotates and translates at the same time. But it is possible to apply a force so that a body does not rotate. Figure 5.3a illustrates how a force applied at C will not produce any rotational acceleration. C is called the centre of mass, and $m_1 d_1 = m_2 d_2$. Figure 5.3b shows parallel gravitational forces acting on the same bodies in a uniform gravitational field.

Figure 5.2

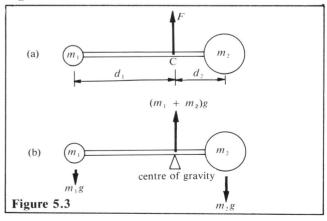

Figure 5.3

Q 5.7 Study question
Define the centre of gravity and use figure 5.3 to explain why it is the same point as the centre of mass in a uniform gravitational field. ■

Q 5.8 Study question
Figure 5.4 shows four equivalent diagrams which illustrate an important theorem. Say why each is equivalent to the next in the sequence and make a statement of the theorem which expresses the fact that figures 5.4a and 5.4d are equivalent. What is the value of T? ■

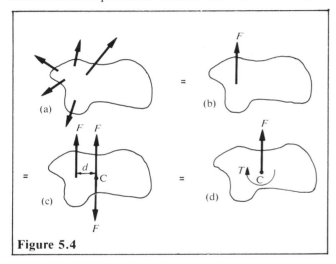

Figure 5.4

5.3 Rotation–translation

Translational acceleration is produced by a force acting through the centre of mass.

Rotational acceleration is the result of a couple acting on the body.

Q 5.9 Study question
Figure 5.5 is a multiflash photograph of the motion of two pucks of equal mass which are joined together as shown. The dots indicate the successive positions of the centre of mass. The motion was started by giving a push to the lower puck only.

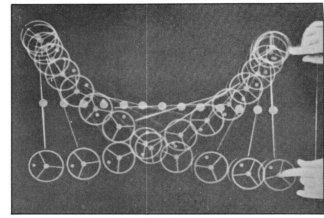

Figure 5.5

(a) Sketch the positions at which you would expect to see the pucks if the photograph continued for another 4 glimpses. Sketch in also the corresponding positions of the centre of mass.

(b) Explain why the centre of mass moves in a straight line while the pucks move in arcs. ■

AV FM 8 Film loop
Centre of mass

This loop investigates the motion of coupled pucks and irregularly shaped bodies when no resultant external force acts on them. The bodies include masses connected by springs, and magnetic pucks which interact with each other, but in all cases the centre of mass of the system obeys the laws of motion derived for a point mass.

Q 5.10 Self-assessment question
(a) Sketch the forces acting on the spinning gyroscope wheel in figure 5.6a.

(b) Why is there no translational motion?

(c) What effect has the force exerted by the string on the axle? Describe the motion of the wheel after the string leaves the axle? Can the thumb be removed now?

(d) What forces act on the wheel nut in figures 5.6b and 5.6c?

(e) Is there any difference in the effects produced by a double-ended or a single-ended spanner? Explain. ■

Figure 5.6a

Figure 5.6b

Figure 5.6c

Q 5.11 Study question

Take a pencil and stand it on its end (figure 5.7). Try flicking it with a finger, first half way down (at A) and then at a point near the base (B).

Explain why the pencil spins in one case but not in the other. ■

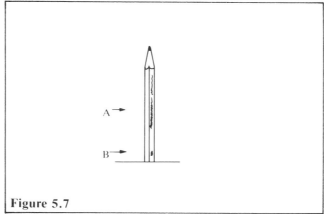

Figure 5.7

Q 5.12 Self-assessment question

A space station shaped like a doughnut has two rocket motors mounted at A and B as shown in figure 5.8. Their directions of thrust are controllable.

(a) How would you use them to set the space station rotating when it has achieved its orbit position?

(b) What would happen if one of the rocket motors failed during the firing? ■

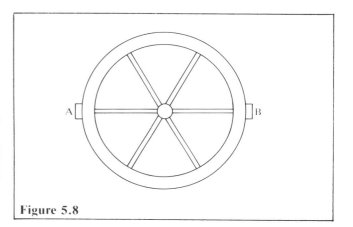

Figure 5.8

5.4 Rotational motion

We have studied the laws dealing with translational motion. Now we consider in detail the rotational effects produced by a couple acting on a body. You have only to watch a plate spinning to realise how complex rotational motion can be. We will deal with the simplest case in which a body is turning or spinning without any wobble. First compare the quantities in linear and rotational dynamics.

Q 5.13 Development question

What is the rotational counterpart of
(a) displacement,
(b) velocity,
(c) acceleration? ■

The basic quantity for recording rotational motion is θ, the angular displacement. Having fixed that, the rest follow:

angular velocity ω is rate of change of θ, or $\dfrac{d\theta}{dt}$

angular acceleration α is the rate of change of ω, or $\dfrac{d\omega}{dt}$

Q 5.14 Self-assessment question

Write down the rotational counterparts of these equations:

(a) average speed $= \dfrac{\text{distance}}{\text{time}}$,

(b) velocity = rate of change of displacement,

(c) $a = \dfrac{v-u}{t}$ for constant linear acceleration,

(d) $v = u + at$ for constant linear acceleration. ■

Q 5.15 Self-assessment question

(a) Calculate the average tangential linear acceleration of a point on the rim of the top shown in figure 5.9 if the rim speed v changes from $10\ \text{m s}^{-1}$ to $20\ \text{m s}^{-1}$ in 5 s.
(b) What is the angular acceleration?
(Give units for both answers.) ■

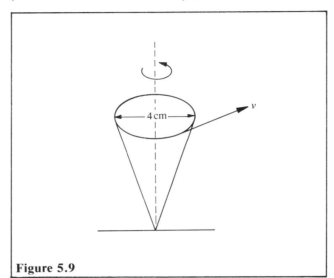

Figure 5.9

E Experiment FM 7
Effect of a torque

This is a quick preliminary investigation to observe how a force applied to a door at different places can cause a change in its angular velocity.

Moment of inertia

Q 5.16 Development question*

A couple of torque T applied to a body gives it a rotational acceleration α about O (figure 5.10). The torque produces tangential forces $F_1, F_2, F_3 \ldots$, acting on particles of the body of masses $m_1, m_2, m_3 \ldots$

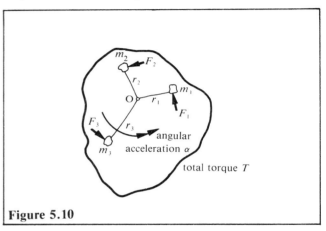

Figure 5.10

(a) Write down the linear acceleration a of mass m_1 in terms of angular acceleration α.
(b) Write in symbols the equation
force = mass × acceleration
for the particle of mass m_1, and so obtain another expression for α.
(c) Use the equations from (a) and (b) to obtain an expression for F_1 in terms of α.
(d) What is the turning moment (torque) of force F_1?
(e) Show that the total torque is given by

$$T = \alpha \ \Sigma \ mr^2$$

where $\Sigma \ mr^2$ means the sum of all quantities such as $m_1 r_1{}^2$.

(f) Σmr^2 defines a quantity called the *moment of inertia* of the body about point 0. $I_0 = \Sigma m r^2$, where r is the distance of a particle from the axis of rotation 0. What is the unit of moment of inertia? ■

We may write Newton's second law applied to rotational motion as:

Torque = moment of inertia×angular acceleration. $T = I\alpha$, compared with $F = ma$ for translational motion. The moment of inertia replaces the inertial mass when we change from linear motion to rotational motion.

Notice that the 'resistance to change' shown by a body which is set spinning by a torque depends on three factors:

1 The mass of the body.
2 The way in which the mass is distributed.
3 The axis considered.

If all the mass is the same distance r from the axis of rotation, as in a ring rotating about its centre, then

$I_O = \Sigma mr^2$
$= m_1 r^2 + m_2 r^2 + m_3 r^2 + \ldots$
$= Mr^2$
$= $ mass of ring×(radius)^2

In all other cases the distance of masses m_1, m_2, etc. varies and it is necessary to use integration methods to calculate the moment of inertia. For example, for a uniform disc, rotating about an axis through the centre O and perpendicular to the plane of the disc,

$$I_O = \tfrac{1}{2} Mr^2$$

You do not need to know how to calculate these moments of inertia, but a general expression can be used for all moments of inertia:

$$I = Mk^2$$

where M is the mass of the body and k is called the *radius of gyration* about a particular axis. For the rotating disc mentioned above

$$k^2 = \frac{r^2}{2} \quad \text{or} \quad k = \frac{r}{\sqrt{2}}.$$

Q 5.17 Self-assessment question
A hi-fi record-player turntable has a mass of 1.28 kg and a radius of gyration about its centre of 25 cm. What is its moment of inertia? What torque will be required to accelerate it up to 33 r.p.m. in 1 second? ■

E Experiment FM 8
Moment of inertia of a disc
In this experiment you will determine the moment of inertia of a disc such as a record-player turntable.

5.5 Angular momentum

Newton's second law states that 'the rate of change of momentum of a body is equal to the resultant force acting on the body and takes place in the direction of that force'. We can modify this statement for rotational motion by introducing torque and angular momentum.

Q 5.18 Development question
Write the counterpart of this statement of Newton's second law for rotational motion. ■

We define angular momentum as

angular momentum $= \dfrac{\text{moment}}{\text{of inertia}} \times \dfrac{\text{angular}}{\text{velocity}}$

$$L = I\omega$$

which makes it completely analogous to linear momentum

$$p = mv$$

Angular momentum is sometimes called 'moment of momentum' since it is the sum of the moments of the linear momentum for all the particles of the body.

Angular momentum $= \Sigma(r \times mv) = \Sigma mr^2\omega = I\omega$

Q 5.19 Development question
The unit of angular momentum is the joule second. Check that this unit is dimensionally the same as the units of $I\omega$.
(Remember that radians measure angles in terms of a ratio of two lengths.)■

5.20 Self-assessment question
If the earth's radius is 6.0×10^6 m and its mass is 6.0×10^{24} kg, calculate the angular momentum possessed by the earth, assuming that it is a sphere of uniform density. (The moment of inertia of a sphere about a diameter is $\frac{2}{5}Mr^2$.) ■

Extending the analogy between rotational and linear motion we might expect

change in angular momentum = torque × time

which, of course, is the equivalent of impulse.

Conservation of angular momentum
If there is no resultant force on a point mass it has constant linear momentum. If there is no resultant torque on a body it has constant angular momentum.

5.21 Self-assessment question
Look back to figure 4.4 in the last chapter.
(a) What is the resultant force, and resultant torque, after the string has been burnt?
(b) Describe the motion of the puck in this period. ■

The angular momentum of the puck is conserved because there is no external torque. This is true not only for an isolated body but for a system of interacting bodies. The law of conservation of angular momentum can be stated as:

'The total angular momentum of a system of interacting bodies about any given axis remains constant provided there is no external torque.'

An interesting consequence of this law is the change in the angular velocity of a body if its moment of inertia changes without any interaction with other bodies. If I increases then ω must decrease for the product $I\omega$ to remain constant.

Figure 5.11

Changing the moment of inertia of a body, as a means of controlling angular velocity, is used in a number of sports. Competitors can change the moment of inertia of their bodies by extending their arms or curling up their bodies. Thus, the rate of spin or roll can be controlled, for example, by a skater or a high-board diver (figure 5.11). The diver takes off with small angular velocity and increases his spin in flight by closing his arms up to his body.

5.22 Self-assessment question
A skater is spinning at 6.0 rad s^{-1} with her arms and one leg outstretched. The spin is increased to 30 rad s^{-1} when she draws her arms and leg in.
(a) Why should the movement in the arms and legs cause this change in spin?
(b) If, with her arms out, her moment of inertia was 5 kg m^2, what was the moment of inertia with her arms and leg drawn in? ■

5.23 Self-assessment question
This question has a mixture of linear and angular momentum in it. See if you can sort them out.

A disc of mass 10 kg is free to rotate about an axis perpendicular to the disc through its centre of mass. The disc is hit by a bullet at its rim, the bullet travelling tangentially to the rim and becoming embedded in the rim. The disc has a radius of 10 cm. The bullet has a mass of 10 g and was moving at 4.0×10^2 m s^{-1}. Assuming the disc to be at rest initially, what will be the angular velocity of the disc? What assumption can you make because the mass of the bullet is small compared to the mass of the disc?
(I for a disc is $\frac{1}{2}Mr^2$ about an axis through the centre perpendicular to the plane of the disc.) ■

Rotational kinetic energy

The analogy between linear and rotational motion suggests that:

rotational kinetic energy $= \frac{1}{2} I \omega^2$

Q 5.24 Study question

A body has a constant angular velocity ω about an axis through O. By considering the linear kinetic energy of its particles, of masses m_1, m_2 . . ., obtain an expression for the rotational kinetic energy. Compare your result with the expression for the kinetic energy of a mass m moving with linear velocity v. ■

This expression shows the factors which determine the rotational kinetic energy. Of course, the principle of conservation of energy doesn't say that rotational energy is conserved, but that mechanical energy is conserved if no dissipative effects occur. So we can apply the principle to energy transfers in which rotational energy is changed because of changes in the potential energy or translation energy of bodies, or when work is done by the rotation of a couple.

Q 5.25 Study question

(a) A force F provides a constant torque which rotates the body through angle θ (figure 5.12). Show that the work done by the torque is $T\theta$.
(b) What are the dimensions and unit of $T\theta$? ■

Q 5.26 Self-assessment question

(a) Calculate the energy stored in a flywheel of mass 5.0 kg and radius 1.0×10^{-1} m, rotating at 1.2×10^3 revolutions per minute about its centre O. You should assume the flywheel to be a uniform disc. ($I_O = M \frac{r^2}{2}$).
(b) What torque would you need to stop it in 10 seconds? ■

Q 5.27 Self-assessment question

A solid cylinder of mass M and radius r rolls from rest down an inclined plane without slipping (figure 5.13). Find its speed (linear) when it reaches the bottom. *Note*: this question can be done using a 'force and torque' method or by an energy method. The energy method is simpler. ■

E Experiment FM 9
Moment of inertia of a flywheel

The angular velocity of a flywheel is measured and the law of conservation of energy is used to calculate its moment of inertia.

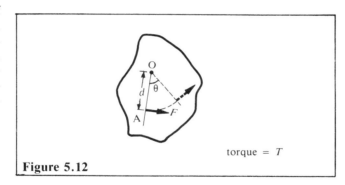

torque = T

Figure 5.12

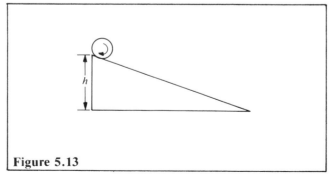

Figure 5.13

Solving problems on rotating bodies

As with linear dynamics, changes in rotational motion can be predicted using momentum considerations, or energy considerations, or both. Remember this as you attempt the following questions, and remember also the key equations for solving problems on rotation.

1 Torque = moment of inertia × angular acceleration
→ $\quad T = I\alpha$

2 Angular impulse = change in angular momentum
→ $\quad Tt = I\omega_2 - I\omega_1$

3 Work done by a torque = change in rotational kinetic energy
→ $\quad T\theta = \frac{1}{2}I\omega_2^2 - \frac{1}{2}I\omega_1^2$
(assuming no energy dissipation)

The summary table in figure 5.14, which compares quantities used in studying linear and rotational motion, will also be useful.

Linear motion		Rotational motion	
distance	s	angle	θ
velocity	$v = \dfrac{\mathrm{d}s}{\mathrm{d}t}$	angular velocity	$\omega = \dfrac{\mathrm{d}\theta}{\mathrm{d}t}$
acceleration	$a = \dfrac{\mathrm{d}v}{\mathrm{d}t}$	angular acceleration	$\alpha = \dfrac{\mathrm{d}\omega}{\mathrm{d}t}$
for constant acceleration	$v = u + at$ $s = ut + \frac{1}{2}at^2$ $v^2 = u^2 + 2as$	for constant angular acceleration	$\omega = \omega_0 + \alpha t$ $\theta = \omega_0 t + \frac{1}{2}\alpha t^2$ $\omega^2 = \omega_0^2 + 2\alpha\theta$
mass (measures linear inertia)	m	moment of inertia (measures rotational inertia)	$I = \Sigma\, mr^2$
force	F	couple or torque	T
momentum	mv	angular momentum	$I\omega$
work	Fs	work	$T\theta$
impulse	Ft	angular impulse	Tt
energy	$\frac{1}{2}mv^2$	energy	$\frac{1}{2}I\omega^2$
equation of motion	$F = ma$ $F = \dfrac{\mathrm{d}(mv)}{\mathrm{d}t}$	equation of motion	$T = I\alpha$ $T = \dfrac{\mathrm{d}(I\omega)}{\mathrm{d}t}$
For a constant force F:		For a constant torque T:	
work done	$Fs = \frac{1}{2}mv_2^2 - \frac{1}{2}mv_1^2$	work done	$T\theta = \frac{1}{2}I\omega_2^2 - \frac{1}{2}I\omega_1^2$
impulse	$Ft = mv_2 - mv_1$	angular impulse	$Tt = I\omega_2 - I\omega_1$

Figure 5.14 Summary: comparison of linear and rotational motion

5.28 Study question

Q Petrol and gas engines incorporate a massive flywheel (figure 5.15). Explain the usefulness of this component in providing a smoother running engine. Why is such a flywheel not needed in electric motors? ■

Figure 5.15

5.29 Self-assessment question

Q When a plane comes in to land, a squeal is heard from the tyres and sometimes a puff of smoke is seen. Suggest a possible explanation of these observations, discussing the changes which occur at the moment of touchdown. Is momentum conserved in this interaction? Explain. ■

Q 5.30 Self-assessment question

(a) Why should car wheels be made as light as possible if high performance is to be achieved?

(b) A car of mass 8.0×10^2 kg has wheels of mass 10 kg each. What proportion of its total kinetic energy is stored in the wheels when it is travelling at velocity v, if each wheel has a diameter of 600 mm and a radius of gyration about the axle of 0.20 m. (Ignore rotational energy in the engine and transmission.) ▪

Q 5.31 Self-assessment question

When a racing car travelling at high speed leaves the track, the driver often puts the car into a spin if he sees that he cannot otherwise bring the car rapidly to a standstill.

(a) Explain how this action helps to stop the car.

(b) Why is there only a small risk of overturning when a racing car goes into a spin on a flat surface?

(c) Under what conditions is a racing car likely to overturn? ▪

Q 5.32 Self-assessment question

Some small toy cars use for propulsion the energy stored in a flywheel; these toys are popularly known as friction powered. Think of a better name for these cars, and write a brief note in which you argue the case for adopting your description. ▪

Comprehension exercise

Building the wind-up tube train

A child's spinning top, known technically as a flywheel, is an efficient energy-storage device. It will be used experimentally for the first time late this year to capture some of the kinetic energy lost when a tube train stops at a station and re-use that energy to start the train again.

In the experiment, a pair of 270 kg, 60 cm steel discs rotating in an evacuated (30 mmHg) chamber will be installed in each of two New York tube carriages. Each carriage will still have its normal electric motors and power-collection system; an electric motor will also be attached to each flywheel. Before beginning a run, the flywheels will be brought up to 14 000 rev/min by their motors. During train acceleration, the flywheel motors will be used as generators to produce electricity for the carriage motors. During braking, all motor fields are reversed and the carriage motors act as generators to power the flywheel motors.

The bulk of the electricity used by a tube system is for accelerating trains out of stations, and the New York Metropolitan Transportation Authority estimates that flywheels could save enough energy from braking to provide half the acceleration energy. The New York underground requires 10% of the city's electricity generating capacity; peak demand in New York City is during the evening rush hour, just when the underground is also consuming the most electricity. Thus, if the flywheel is successful, it could reduce power consumption just at the time of day when there is least spare capacity.

Energy-storing flywheels are not new — they have been used to power torpedoes since 1870 and are used for industrial applications such as punch presses where power surges are needed without putting a drain on the electrical system.

But there has been interest recently in 'regenerative' flywheels for vehicles because of the demand for pollution control, studies of hybrid vehicles, and the improving flywheel technology. At present, flywheels such as those to be used in New York store as much energy per kilogram as the best available batteries. But battery technology has been pushed to the limit, with no significant improvements in sight for the near future, while available technology could more than double the energy storage capacity of the flywheel, and research has really only just begun.

A flywheel has been tried in a vehicle before — the Swiss Electrogyro Omnibus successfully carried passengers from 1953 until 1969. But the flywheel was the sole source of power — effectively it was a wind-up bus — which limited its range. The flywheel only stored one-fifth the energy of present systems, so the bus had to stop at a 'power-point' every half mile to speed up the flywheel again. Recently interest has switched to more practical hybrids, such as the New York underground carriages, where a traditional motor provides normal running power and the flywheel provides acceleration boosts.

Although simple in theory, the flywheel has a large number of technical problems. Rapidly spinning objects are subject to many forces — for example, if the flywheel is horizontal and rotates clockwise, when the vehicle drives uphill the gyroscopic couple generated forces the flywheel to the left. (In the New York underground carriage, this effect is avoided by mounting the flywheel vertically under the floor, which restricts its size.)

Gravitational effects will cause the flywheel to want to precess like a gyroscope. And there is the danger that, during a skid, the vehicle will counter rotate around the flywheel axis. Thus one is forced to employ complicated gimbaled mountings or to use two oppositely rotating flywheels on the same shaft.

The need for a vacuum to reduce drag means that either the flywheel bearings must be airtight, or a magnetic suspension system must be employed, or a vacuum pump must be included.

Finally, the rapidly spinning flywheel could be a serious danger in event of an accident. Researchers at the Johns Hopkins University Applied Physics Laboratory recently concluded that 'it is not feasible' to use flywheel systems in which the flywheel case is used to absorb all of the flywheel energy in case of accident. Instead, they propose using a brittle composite material made of glass or graphite that would be self-pulverising in event of failure.

(From an article by Dr. J. Hanlon, 'Building the wind-up tube train,' in *New Scientist*, 10 February, 1972).

Questions

1 Re-phrase the second sentence, explaining in more precise scientific language the phrases 'to capture kinetic energy' and 're-use energy'.

2 Calculate how much energy will be stored by the flywheels before the train starts (paragraph 2). (The moment of inertia of a flywheel is $\frac{1}{2}Mr^2$).

3 If all this energy is used to accelerate a train of mass 1.0×10^4 kg, what speed will it acquire? Comment on your answer. (The moment of inertia of a flywheel is $\frac{1}{2}Mr^2$).

4 Why is the chamber containing the flywheel evacuated? What design features are suggested for maintaining this low pressure around the flywheels?

5 Explain the different functions of 'carriage motors' and 'flywheel motors'. When is one of these types of motor required to act as a generator? How is this possible?

6 How is it possible to increase the energy per kilogram stored by a flywheel, and how might modern technology be used to increase this quantity?

7 How did the Swiss 'wind-up bus' system function and what was the limitation of this system? Why, in contrast, is the New York system described as a 'practical hybrid?'

8 Why might a flywheel system be dangerous? How can this danger be minimised?

Questions on objectives

1 For each of the statements in parts (a)–(d) choose one of the following terms (A–D) with which it is closely associated:

A couple,
B angular momentum,
C moment of inertia,
D centre of mass.

(a) A couple acting on a rigid body changes this.
(b) The measure of the resistance of a body to change in angular velocity or rotational motion.
(c) The point through which a force must act if no torque is produced.
(d) A pair of parallel forces acting in opposite directions is called this.

(objectives 1 and 2)

2 Below are two lists, one of units (A–E) and one of symbols (1–5). For each of the terms (a)–(e) decide which of A–E and which of 1–5 apply to it.

A rad s^{-1}	1 I
B N m	2 p
C kg m s^{-1}	3 L
D kg m^2 s^{-1}	4 ω
E kg m^2	5 T

(a) Angular momentum.
(b) Moment of inertia.
(c) Torque.
(d) Linear momentum.
(e) Angular velocity.

(objective 3)

3 Show that a force acting on a body along a given line which is not through its centre of mass can be replaced by a force of the same magnitude, acting through the centre of mass, together with a couple. What is the effect on the motion of the body of:
(a) a force through the centre of mass,
(b) a couple?

(objectives 4 and 5)

4 A flywheel of moment of inertia 0.30 kg m^2 is rotated steadily at 100 rad s^{-1} by a 50 W electric motor.
(a) Find the kinetic energy of the flywheel.
(b) Calculate the value of the frictional couple opposing the rotation.
(c) If the motor is switched off, calculate the angular acceleration of the flywheel as it slows down.
(d) Find the time taken for the wheel to come to rest after the motor has been switched off.

(objectives 8 and 9)

5 A bicycle wheel spinning in a vertical plane (i.e. about a horizontal axis through its centre) is lowered on to a plank of wood resting on ice. The plank and wheel have each a mass of 1.0 kg. The mass of the wheel is concentrated around the rim and the radius of the wheel is 60 cm. If the angular velocity of the wheel just before it touched the plank was 7.0 rad s^{-1}, estimate its angular velocity after contact with the wood, and the velocity of the wood across the ice. What is the total change in kinetic energy?

(Hint: assume the plank and wheel are in contact for a very short time t. What can you say about the force of the wheel on the plank and the force of the plank on the wheel during this time? What can you say about the impulses produced?)

(objectives 7 and 9)

6 Six men, all of about the same weight, stand at regular intervals around the circumference of a turntable, each being 2.5 m from the axis. The turntable is given a speed of 2 revolutions per minute. At a signal, all six men simultaneously move inwards, to take up new positions each 0.5 m from the axis. Calculate:
(a) the new speed of the turntable,
(b) the ratio of the new to the old energy of the system. Comment on the result.
(Neglect the mass of the turntable, and frictional losses).

(objectives 6, 7 and 9)

Appendix

Revision work

References to relevant chapters of O level text books are given in each section. Use these references in answering the questions and in checking that you understand the relevant pre-requisite objectives. Answers are given in the 'Answers' section for questions marked *.

Section A Forces

References:
Abbott   Chapters 2 and 4
Ashurst   Chapters 3 and 4
Duncan PTT   Chapters 25, 26, 27
Harrison R. D. *Forces.*

Use the references listed above in answering the following questions.

Q A 1 Define the moment of a force and state the law of moments for parallel forces. Outline the method you would use to measure the mass of an apple, given a metre rule, some string and a 100 gram 'weight'. ■

Q A 2 Make a list of as many different types of force as you can find, writing a short note on the cause of each. ■

Q A 3 Sketch figure P1 (preliminary test) and mark in arrows to show the direction and points of application of the forces acting on the runner. Label the arrows with the names of the forces. ■

Refer back to pre-requisite objectives 1 and 2 to confirm that you have now achieved these objectives.

Section B Vectors

References:
Abbott   Chapter 3 (force as a vector) and
                Chapter 5 (parallelogram of velocities)
Ashurst   Chapter 3
Duncan PTT   Chapter 27
Jardine   Chapter 15

Use the references above to help you answer the following questions.

Q A 4 Explain the terms vector and scalar and give two examples of each. ■

Q A 5 Sketch and explain a graphical method for (a) adding, and (b) subtracting two vectors of the same kind. ■

Q A 6* A man is cycling at a constant speed of 10 kilometres per hour. At a given instant he is travelling due north; at a later time he has changed his direction to 60° east of north. Make a scale drawing, indicating directions by arrows, to represent these two velocities of the cyclist, and deduce the change in *velocity*. ■

Q A 7* Forces of 30 newtons and 70 newtons are used to support a hanging weight of 80 newtons. At what angle to the vertical does each of the two forces act? ■

Q A 8* Rain is falling vertically at 8.0 metres per second. The raindrops make tracks on the side window of a car at an angle of 35° below the horizontal. Calculate the speed of the car if it is travelling on a horizontal road. ■

Refer back to pre-requisite objectives 3, 4, 5 and 6 to confirm that you have now achieved these objectives.

Section C Kinematics

References:
Abbott   Chapter 5
Ashurst   Chapter 8
Duncan PTT   Chapters 35, 36, 37
Jardine   Chapter 6

Use the references listed above to help you to answer the following questions.

Q A 9* Explain the difference between average velocity and instantaneous velocity. The graph in figure A1 shows the motion of a car over a period of time.
(a) What is its maximum velocity?
(b) What is its initial acceleration?
(c) How far did it travel during the first ten seconds? ■

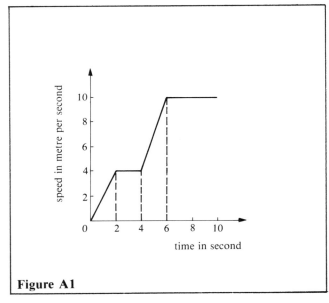

Figure A1

Q A 10 Explain the meaning of uniform acceleration. For a body which starts from rest and has a uniform acceleration a, deduce expressions for
(a) the velocity acquired in a time t,
(b) the velocity acquired in a distance s.

Q A 11* A train moves from rest with an acceleration of 0.5 metre per second squared. Find the speed in metres per second, and kilometres per hour, which it reaches in moving through its own length, which is 100 metres. ■

Q A 12* A stone is thrown horizontally with an initial velocity of 15 metres per second from a tower 20 metres high.
(a) How long does it take to reach the ground?
(b) At what distance from the base of the tower does it reach the ground? ■

Work through one of the following if they are available:

AV **FM 1 Film loop**
    Distance, Time and Speed

AV **FM 2 Film loop**
    One dimensional acceleration

AV **FM 3 Film loop**
    Trajectories

C **Computer programme**
   KINERV
You should consult the teacher in charge of the computer terminal for instructions on how to log on.

Refer back to pre-requisite objectives 7, 8 and 9 to confirm that you have now achieved these objectives.

Section D Work, energy and power
References:
Abbott   Chapter 7
Ashurst   Chapter 5
Duncan PTT   Chapters 28 and 40
Jardine   Chapters 9 and 19

Use the references listed above to help you answer the following questions.

Q A 13 Explain the terms work, potential energy, kinetic energy and power. Define a unit for each in the SI system. ■

Q A 14* A railway engine pulls a train at a steady speed of 72 kilometres per hour along a level track. The tension in the coupling between the coaches and engine is 5×10^4 newtons. What power, in watts, is being used to pull the coaches? ■

Q A 15* What additional power would be required to pull the coaches up a slope of 1 in 200 at the same speed, if their mass is 5×10^5 kilograms? ■

Q A 16* The time taken for a neutron to travel 6.0 metres in a straight line is 0.3 millisecond. If a neutron has a mass of 5×10^{-26} kilogram, calculate its kinetic energy. ■

Q A 17* A cricket ball of mass 0.15 kilogram is thrown vertically upwards with an initial velocity of 20 metres per second. If the ball reaches a maximum vertical displacement of 16 metres, what is the percentage loss of energy caused by air resistance? ■

Refer back to pre-requisite objectives 10, 11, 12 and 13 to confirm that you have now achieved these objectives.

Experiment FM1 Motion due to a steady force

Aim

The experiment investigates how the acceleration of a body of fixed mass depends on the applied force, and how the same force produces different accelerations for bodies of different masses.

Apparatus

- ticker-timer, carbon disc and paper tape
- 6-12 V a.c. power supply
- 3 trolleys (or 1 trolley and 2 or more stackable masses)
- 4 elastic cords
- runway

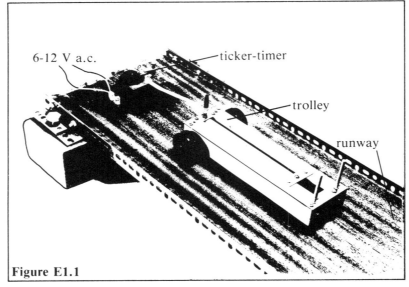

6-12 V a.c. ticker-timer

trolley

runway

Figure E1.1

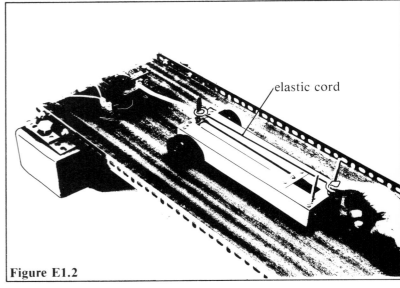

elastic cord

Figure E1.2

1   The ticker-tape records the distance travelled in intervals of 1/50 s. Pass a length of ticker-tape through the vibrator of the timer and attach it to the back of a trolley, as shown in figure E1.1. Adjust the slope of the runway so that frictional forces are balanced by the component of gravitational force down the runway. The runway is then friction-compensated, the trolley moves at constant speed after an initial push, and the dots on the tape are equally spaced.

2   A length of elastic cord stretched by a fixed amount is used to provide a unit of force.

Pull the trolley down the runway keeping the extension of the elastic fixed, as in figure E 1.2. Experiment with a few trial runs before switching on the vibrator. Mark this tape mass 1, force 1.

3   Repeat the trolley run using two stretched elastic cords to give a force of 2 units acting on the trolley. Mark this tape mass 1, force 2. Then obtain two more tapes, using forces of 3 and 4 units.

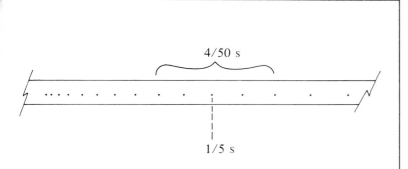

4/50 s

1/5 s

Figure E1.3

4   Use your tapes to plot speed-time graphs for each run.
Note. It is not possible to measure instantaneous speed with apparatus available in school laboratories, so the graph will be a plot of average speeds against time. You can record these average speeds by:
(a) cutting the tape into ten-tick lengths to produce a chart which records average speeds in consecutive periods of 1/5 second, or
(b) taking measurements directly on the tape to find the average speed around a particular time, e.g. average speed during 4/50 s around 1/5 s (figure E1.3). It is obviously not very accurate to measure speed from the space between consecutive dots. Why?

You may decide to measure average speeds in different ways for different tapes because the speeds vary. Make a note in your experimental report to say why you used a particular method of calculating average speeds.

5   Use your graphs to answer the following questions.
(a) Is the acceleration constant when a constant force is applied?
(b) What are the accelerations for each of the forces you used?
(c) What relationship between force and acceleration is shown by your experimental results?

6   Now obtain ticker-tape records of the motions of different masses pulled by the same force. For example, use two stretched elastic cords to pull one trolley, then two stacked trolleys, then three. Why is it necessary to adjust the friction-compensation of the runway when different masses are used?

7   Calculate the acceleration for each run. Is it permissible to calculate acceleration by applying the equation $s = \frac{1}{2}at^2$, or some other equation, to the motion recorded on your tape? What justified assumptions would you make?

8   What relationship between acceleration and mass, when the same force acts on different masses, is suggested by your results?

Experiment FM2 Conservation of momentum

Aim

In this experiment you will investigate the changes in velocity which occur when bodies collide or spring apart, and calculate how the total momentum of the system is affected by such interactions.

Apparatus

- 2 trolleys (one with a spring plunger)
- masses, or additional trolleys, for increasing the colliding masses
- trolley runway
- ticker-timer with carbon discs and paper tape
- 6-12 V a.c. power supply
- plasticine, cork and large pin

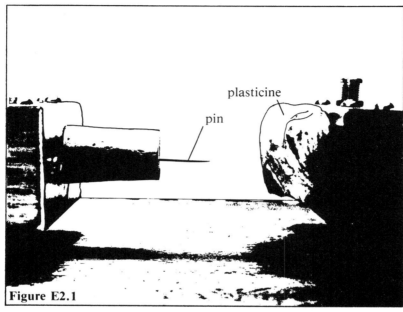

plasticine

pin

Figure E2.1

Note. Many experiments can be used to study momentum changes. The interactions studied may be explosions or collisions. The bodies may stick together after collision, or move separately. The interacting bodies may be trolleys, frictionless pucks, or vehicles on a linear air track. You may do the experiment outlined here or some other. Whatever method you choose, begin by considering the following questions. (There are no 'right' answers to these questions, but thinking about them will help you to design an effective experiment.)

(a) Does the force of gravity produce a momentum change?

(b) How can you ensure that interaction caused by friction will not affect your measurements?

(c) To measure momentum changes, you will need to measure masses and velocities. What methods are there for measuring velocities on the scale of this experiment?
What factors limit the scale of the experiment?
Would a larger scale experiment be more accurate?

(d) What factor is likely to have most effect on the accuracy of the experiment?

1 Investigate the velocity and momentum changes which occur when a trolley moving down a runway at a constant velocity collides with a stationary trolley so that the two trolleys stick together (figure E2.1).
Is it necessary to compensate the runway for friction?
Will ticker-tape be adequate for recording all the velocities?

2 Repeat the experiment using different colliding masses, by stacking several trolleys together or adding stackable masses. Make sure that additional masses are fixed in position so that they move as one mass during the interaction.

3 Make a 'balance sheet' by drawing up a table as shown below. You do not need to work in absolute units. Mass can be expressed in multiples of trolley units, velocity in cm per tick.

Before collision			After collision		
moving mass	velocity	momentum	moving mass	velocity	momentum

4 Now investigate *elastic* collisions between a trolley moving with constant velocity and a stationary one.